A Seaman's Guide to
BASIC CHARTWORK

C000281239

A Seaman's Guide to
BASIC CHARTWORK

MORGANS TECHNICAL BOOKS LIMITED
P.O. Box 5,
Wotton- under- Edge,
Gloucestershire. GL12 7BY

© MORGANS TECHNICAL BOOKS LIMITED 1985

ISBN 0 948254 01 7

2nd Edition 1989

This programme was revised by Malcolm Skene, Roy Kenyon and Ken Elliott of the LOMER NAUTICAL COLLEGE, QUEEN'S CRESCENT, SOUTHSEA.

The extracts from Admiralty Charts 5050 & L(DI) 5050 are used in the text and on the covers of this book and are reproduced with the sanction of the Controller of Her Majesty's Stationery Office and of the Hydrographer of the Navy.

Printed in Great Britain by View Publications (Bristol) Ltd.

Foreword

by
**Sir Gilmour Jenkins
KCB KBE MC**

**Chairman, Seafarers
Education Service.**

**Formerly, Permanent
Secretary to the
Ministry of Transport
and Civil Aviation.**

and
A. G. Watson

**Captain, Royal Navy,
H.M.S. DRYAD
Royal Naval School
of Navigation and
Aircraft Direction.**

The prime duty of the Navigating Officer, after he has satisfied himself that his ship is on her proper course, is to ensure that she is navigated with complete safety, avoiding all hazards whether natural or man-made, static or moving. This demands skilled seamanship, involving the ability to assess, reliably and consistently, what the ship's position is at the moment and what it will be after a short interval of time. In coastal and in crowded waters the result must be arrived at not only with a high degree of accuracy but also at high speed.

To teach the student the way to do it, the Royal Navy and the Merchant Navy, following the success of A SEAMAN'S GUIDE TO THE RULE OF THE ROAD, have again worked together, using the same technique of programmed instruction, to produce a similar guide, this time on the use of the Chart. The book provides instruction both in the principles of navigation and in the way to use, with speed and accuracy, all the various techniques involved in putting those principles into practice. The method is to involve the student, from the beginning, in the solution of practical problems and to allow the principles to emerge naturally from the practice.

It makes a worthy companion to the earlier volume.

Acknowledgements

We should like to acknowledge the detailed and constructive help given in this project by Lieutenant Commander M. J. Larmuth and the Navigation Instructional Staff of the Britannia Royal Naval College, Dartmouth; and by Mr. A. Carver and Mr. M. M. Cornish of the Plymouth College of Technology.

Our thanks are also due to Lieutenant Commander S. L. Morse, Canadian Forces, of the Royal Naval Programmed Instruction Unit, HMS Collingwood; Lieutenant Commander G. C. Marshall of HMS Dryad, for advice and assistance; to the Captain, Britannia Royal Naval College, Dartmouth, for making Royal Naval cadets available for validation; to Captain T. G. Nelson of the School of Maritime Studies, Plymouth College of Technology, for making Merchant Navy cadets available for validation; and finally to Instructor Commander D. E. Cripps and to the departments of the Ministry of Defence (Navy), and in particular the Hydrographer of the Navy, who have been concerned in this project and who have been unfailingly helpful.

Preface

This book was written at the request of the Ministry of Defence (Navy) and has been compiled and validated with the full support and cooperation of the Royal Navy, both the School and the Department of Maritime Studies of the Plymouth College of Technology, and the Seafarers Education Service and College of the Sea.

Aim of the book

The book is designed to teach seafarers the basic techniques of chartwork as a necessary preliminary to the practice of navigation.

The place of the book in teaching navigation

The book is designed to teach only the techniques of plotting, and its use alone will not enable the student to make a safe passage.

It is recommended that the book is used as part of a course given by an instructor with practical sea experience, a course which should give some explanation of, at least, the following points:

continued

The place of the book in teaching navigation (continued)

1. Functions of the officer of the watch, or navigating officer, in ensuring the safety of the ship.

2. Accuracy and reliability of equipment and methods used for fixing the ship.

3. Procedure for fixing.

4. Forecasting and assessment of tidal stream.

5. Meanings of all chart symbols, particularly those relating to depths.

Any course should then be followed by practice at sea.

Previous knowledge assumed

1. Knowledge of which scale is latitude and which is longitude.

2. Knowledge that distance is measured from the latitude scale at the latitude where the measurement is being made.

Previous knowledge assumed (continued)

3. Ability to use parallel rulers and dividers in laying off a course.

4. A general knowledge of sea terms.

5. Ability to relate appearance of the coastline to appearance of the chart.

A student who does not have this knowledge could use the programme but would find more difficulty in starting.

Equipment needed by the student

Set of transparencies and deviation table as supplied with the book.

Chart 5050 and/or
Chart L(D1) 5050
Parallel ruler
Dividers

Decca interpolator (optional)
B or 2B pencil
Rubber
Large pair of compasses

Availability of the book

In the Royal Navy, the book is available through official channels. Merchant Navy personnel can obtain the book from:

Nautical Bookshops

Contents

continued

Contents
(continued)

Validation

This programme has been tested on three groups of cadets undergoing pre-sea training for the Royal Navy and Merchant Navy. The post-programme test consisted of a practical chartwork exercise; marks were allocated both for accuracy of plotting and for knowledge of the principles involved.

In the test 90% of the students obtained 85·9% of marks. The average study time was 12 hours 5 minutes.

The students were in the first month of training and had never been to sea; their average age was 19, and average educational attainment — 2 'A' levels.

In work done after the programme and the test, students showed a very considerable increase in accuracy and an improved grasp of principles, compared with previous standards at this stage of training.

Note to the Instructor

While the students are working through the programme, you should be available to answer questions and, if required, relate the work done on the chart to practical navigation. The programme has been written to be used with an instructor and your assistance and supervision is a very important part of the course.

The layout of the deviation table may not be familiar to you. It is hoped that this new layout will supersede the old one; meanwhile, an explanation is given on pages 244 to 250 of the programme.

Note to the Student

The transparencies are for use as overlays to the chart in order to check your plotting as directed in the programme. You may find fractional disagreement between the transparency and your plotting even after careful checking. This will probably be due to slight distortion of the thin paper on which the special instructional charts are printed.

How to use the programme

Each page is divided up like this:

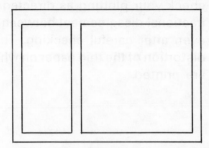

The text, followed by a question, is on the right-hand side of each page. The answer to the question from the previous page is always in the left-hand column. (Look at page 4 for an example.) It is advised that a piece of card be used to cover up the right-hand page of each opening whilst the left-hand page is being read.

The answer may be a reproduction of part of the chart, in which case identify the area of the chart and check that the positions you have plotted are correct.

When you are told to place a transparency on the chart, first align it *carefully* with the reference points marked on the transparency.

Chapter 1

This programme will teach you how to plot your ship's position on a chart.

You will need:
Chart 5050 and/or Chart L(D1) 5050
Parallel rule
Dividers
Large pairs of compasses (8–10 inch)
B or 2B pencil
Eraser
Decca Interpolator (Optional)
Speed-Time-Distance Rule (Optional)

If you have all these ready, and the chart open, then if you are using:

(a) a rolling parallel ruler, go to 2.

(b) an expanding parallel ruler, go to 3.

When drawing a line with the aid of a rolling parallel ruler you must always make sure that this line passes exactly through the scale graduation or object concerned.

Practise this now, by following these instructions:

1. Align your ruler to the parallel of 50°00′N.

2. Roll it to 50°00′·6N.

3. Tilt the ruler away from you until the edge touches the paper, like this:

4. Put your pencil against the edge of the ruler, and adjust the ruler until your pencil point is exactly on 50°00′·6N.

5. Draw a short line through 50°00′·6N on the scale.

Go to 4.

When drawing a line with the aid of an expanding parallel ruler you must always make sure that this line passes exactly through the scale graduation or object concerned.

Practise this now, by following these instructions:

1.   Align your ruler to the parallel of 50°00′N.

2.   Move one arm to 50°00′·6N.

3.   Put your pencil against the edge of the ruler, and adjust the ruler until your pencil point is exactly on 50°00′·6N.

4.   Draw a short line through 50°00′·6N on the scale.

Go to 4.

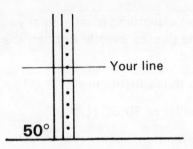

Your line

50°

If your line is not exactly as
this is, rub it out and draw it
again.

Did you use either a crayon
or a pen to draw this line?
If you did you were wrong—
you must use *only* a B or a
2 B pencil on the chart.

Always use your ruler in this way.

Now practise using your dividers <u>accurately.</u>

Set your dividers on to the distance between 05°00'·8W and
the nearest meridian marked on the chart, and then transfer them to
the parallel of 50°00'N, and mark off the longitude on that parallel.

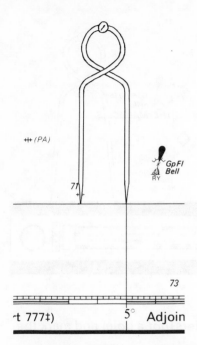

If the point of your dividers was not exactly as shown above, re-set them and try again.

Now plot this position: 50°01'·7N
05°01'·1W.

Do it like this:

First, mark your latitude in pencil.

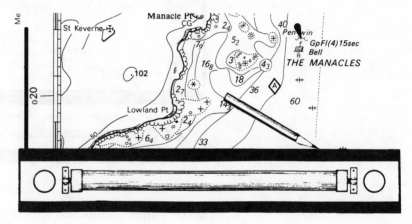

Now plot your longitude like this:

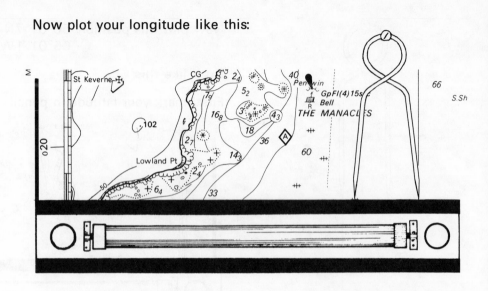

Make a light depression with the dividers (*not* a hole) and mark the position with a cross.

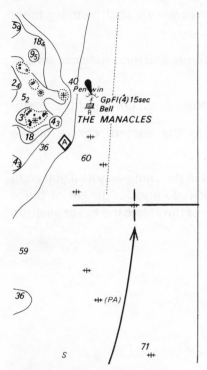

If your position was not exactly here, rub it out and plot it again.

Plot this position:

    50°08'·7N
    04°56'·2W.

Ensure that your pencil line and the dividers' mark are exactly on the latitude and longitude.

Mark the position with a cross.

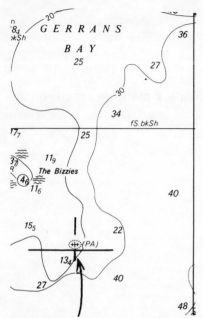

GERRANS
BAY

The Bizzies

If your position was not exactly here, rub it out and plot it again.

Remember where these two positions are — we shall be using them again.

Now, some practice in measuring latitude and longitude accurately. Look for these objects:

1. Mevagissey Light (in the north-west corner of the chart).

2. Eddystone Rocks Light (to the eastern centre of the chart).

Using your parallel ruler and dividers in the same way as if you were plotting a position, measure the latitude and longitude of these lights to the nearest 0′·1. (The centre of the star is the exact position of the light.)

Mevagissey Lt
50°16'·1N
04°46'·9W

Eddystone Rocks Lt
50°10'·8N
04°15'·9W

If you did not measure these positions correctly to the nearest 0'·1, measure them again.

You may also have to plot a position which is given as a range and bearing of a charted object.

Like this: Dodman Point Cross bore 320°–2'·7.

Move your ruler so that the edge passes exactly through 320°, the centre dot of the compass rose and the reciprocal bearing.

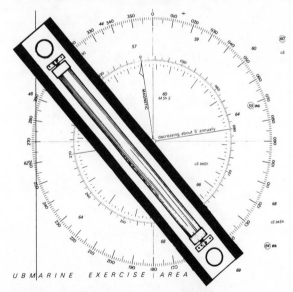

What is the reciprocal of 320°?

140°

(If you did not know it before, the reciprocal of a bearing is the bearing plus or minus 180°.)

Move the ruler so that the edge is exactly over the position of the cross

Now return it to the compass rose.

Is it still exactly aligned as before?

Yes. Go to 11.

No. Go to 12.

Your ruler is exactly aligned
as before.

Good. Your chart is absolutely flat with no bits of rubber or other material on it, and the table top is quite smooth.

Go to 13.

Your ruler is not exactly aligned as before.

Check that your chart is absolutely flat, with no bits of rubber or other material on it, and that the table top is quite smooth.

If you have checked this, and the ruler will still not roll accurately (or transfer accurately in the case of an expanding ruler), call your instructor.

When all is well, go to 13.

Return your ruler to Dodman Point Cross (still on the bearing of 320°), and draw a short line about 3′ away from the cross. (Remember, Dodman Point bore 320° <u>from you</u>, so the line is drawn in the direction 140° from the cross.

Set your dividers to 2'·7 and with one point exactly on the position of Dodman Point Cross make a small depression on the line of bearing that you have just drawn.

Mark this with a cross.

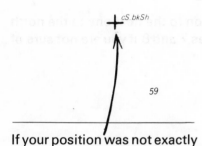

If your position was not exactly here, rub it out and plot it again.

Practise this once more.

The bearing and range given are:-

Gribben Head Daymark bears 300° - 4'·6. (That is Gribben Head bears 300° from you.)

Plot this and mark the point with a cross.

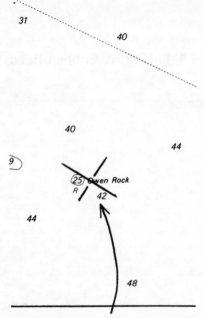

31

40

40

44

9

25 Owen Rock
R
42

44

48

If your position is not exactly here, rub it out and plot it again.

You have plotted four positions.

We will assume that these are four positions that you have planned to pass through on a journey.

Having decided on the positions, your next step is to find the course and speed necessary to pass through them.

First, join the most southerly popsition to the next one to the north (check back to the diagrams on pages 7 and 8 if you are not sure of the positions).

What course is this?

024°
(Not 204°; remember you are starting from the southerly position.)

Draw an arrow on the course in the direction that you will steam and write the course alongside it, like this:

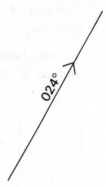

Now join the second position to the third and the third position to the fourth.

Note the courses alongside the lines.

071°
052°

Plot the courses again if you were wrong.

You have now found the courses to steer for the first part of your journey.

The rest of this programme will assume that you are under way, steaming round to Plymouth.

You must record certain aspects of the journey in your notebook, as well as on the chart. Take your notebook and rule it up like this:

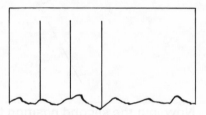

The first column is for noting the time of an event.

The second and third columns are for noting alterations of course and speed.

The fourth column is for recording the position and for noting alterations of course and speed (or for comments such as 'gyro failed').

At 0900 your position is:

50°01'·7N
05°01'·1W
Course 024°, speed 12 knots

Head a page in your notebook with today's date, and record your position, course and speed (use a pencil, not a pen).

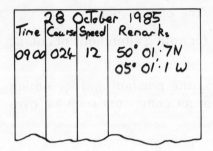

If you entered this wrongly, rub it out and write it again.

(You should head each new page of your notebook with the words:

Time Course Speed Remarks).

From now on, whenever you take a fix, or alter course or speed, you must record it in the notebook <u>before</u> plotting.

Note the time 0900 against your position on the chart, and mark off your position every 15 minutes until 0930. (Remember, your speed is 12 knots — so every 15 minutes you will steam 3 miles.)

Mark each position with a short line across your course and time like this:

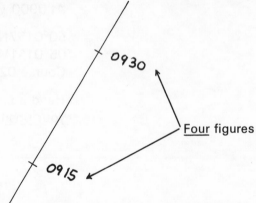

Lay transparency 1 over your course.

If your positions are not accurate, check them, and, if necessary, rub them out and plot them again.

The time is now 0900 and you have just passed through the 0900 position.

The positions that you have marked on the chart up to 0930 are called DEAD RECKONING positions (DR for short); they are always marked with crosses, and_____ – figure times.

four

Your Dead Reckoning positions are based on the speed and direction that the ship is steaming <u>through the water</u>— there may be tidal streams or other factors affecting the ship, but the DR does not take that into account.

So we can say that the DR is worked out using the course and speed_____ the_____.

through   water

To digress for a moment; you may be interested to know the origin of the phrase — Dead Reckoning.

It is generally assumed that it came about like this: in the days of sail, you deduced your reckoning by estimating your course and speed, over the previous 24 hours, usually at the time of the noon sun sight.

The Deduced Reckoning position was entered in the log as Ded. Reckoning — and Ded. being spoken as 'dead', eventually came to be written thus.

The DR position gives only the *approximate* position of the ship, as it does not take into account tidal stream or other effects, but is worked out using the course and speed_____the_____.

through   water

Your DR speed is the speed ordered for the engines or that obtained from the log (which is the instrument that measures speed through the water).

Imagine for a moment that you are the navigating officer of a ship steaming along the courses you have plotted on the chart between 0900 and 0930. You have plotted your DR positions using the course steered and the speed set.

You reach your DR position at 0930 on time, and alter course at 0938½.

If you then change speed, what would you do to the DR position that you have plotted ahead on the chart?

You will have to rub out the symbols showing the DR positions and the times, and plot them again using the new speed.

The speed ordered for the engines may not always be the same as the speed measured by the log. In this case you accept the DR speed as that measured by the log, because it is operated by the speed of the water passing the ship, hence showing the ship's speed_____the_____.

through   water

Now consider the DR course:

The DR course must always represent the true course steered.

Therefore, if a check revealed a gyro-compass error (which obviously would affect the direction in which the ship was steering) how would you work out the DR course?

By adding or subtracting the error of the gyro-compass before plotting the course.

This ensures that the direction in which the ship is steaming through the water is transferred accurately to the chart.

Let us now summarise these points.

DR positions are obtained by plotting the course steered and speed through the water.

Which of the following factors do we apply to the speed and to the course steered in order to work out the DR?

1. Tidal stream

2. Gyro error

3. Ocean currents

Gyro error
(Obviously, this will only be
applied to the course.)

You have learnt how to plot your DR position – the <u>forecast</u> of your ship's position.

In Chapter 2 you will find out how to plot your <u>actual</u> position, when it is known.

Chapter 2

If you took a visual gyro-compass bearing of a fixed point at 1000,

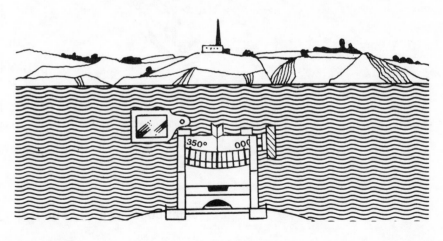

would you obtain the same bearing if you observed the same object at 1010?

No
(Unless you were steering
directly towards, or away
from, the object.)

If you then identified the object, and drew a line on the chart showing the bearing of 355° passing through the church, like this:

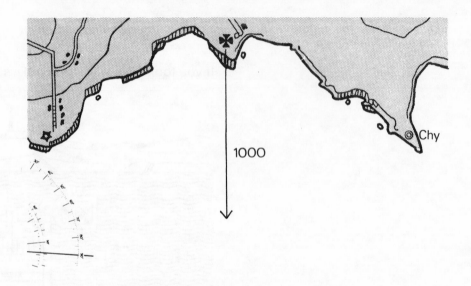

what could you say about the position of the ship at 1000?

It must have been somewhere on the line drawn on the chart.
(In your own words.)

Such a line is called a 'position line'. If you observed two objects at as nearly the same time as possible and so obtained two simultaneous position lines, like this:

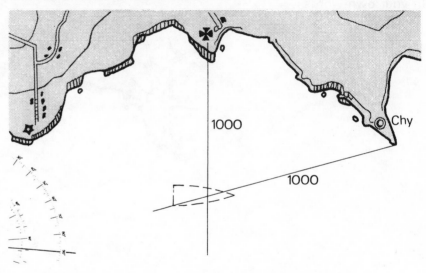

what could you deduce about your position at 1000?

The ship must have been
where the position lines
cross.
(In your own words.)

For reasons which you will learn shortly, we normally take three
bearings to fix the ship's position, and this is known as a 'fix'.

On this picture we have also put in your forecast DR position.

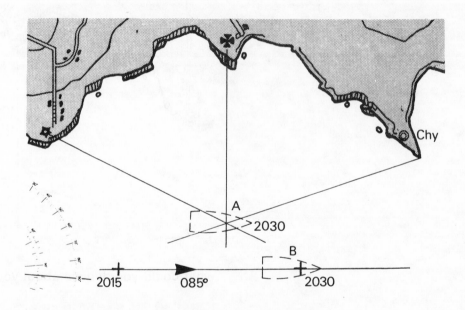

At 2030, which position do you think your ship would actually be in,
A or B?

A
(That is, the point where the
position lines cross.)

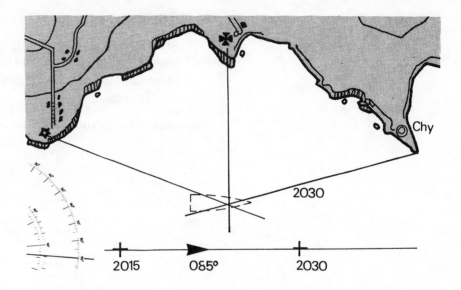

The 2030 DR position is only where you <u>forecast</u> that you would be, but due to small human errors, small errors of equipment and the effect of wind and water movements, you have not quite ended up there.

If at 2030 you take bearings of the three objects, which are in fixed positions, then, if the three bearings cross in a point, this must define your position relative to the three objects.

You have thus <u>fixed</u> your position at_____(what time?).

2030

At 0930 you take these three visual bearings to fix your position:

> St. Anthony's Head   298°
> Gerrans Church   344½°
> Mawnan House   259½°
>   (conspic)

You have already rules up your notebook, enter this fix in it now.

0930	024°	12	ST Anthony Hd.
			298°
			Gerrans Church
			344½°
			Mawnan House
			259½°

Now that you have noted the fix, the next thing to do is plot it.

You should:

Plot the bearings.
Put arrow heads on the ends, pointing *away* from the marks.
Mark where the bearings cross with the symbol ⊙.
Put a four-figure time against it.

Your fix should look like this:

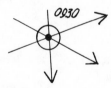

Do this now.

This is the fix:

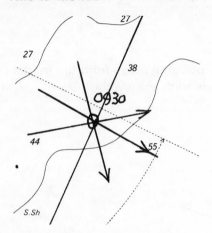

If your fix was not like this, rub it out and plot it again, being very careful to align the ruler correctly.

> Note that you should not draw the whole position line but only about one inch of it to give the fix.

(Let us remind you that the edge of the ruler should not be right on the mark, but far enough away for the pencil line to pass through it.)

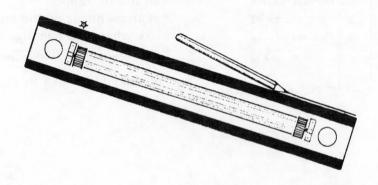

The symbol ⊙ (which you have just plotted) indicates a_____.

fix

At 0938½ you altered course to 071°. (Remember to enter it in your notebook, and use the abbreviation 'a/c' for 'altered course'.)

You take this fix at 1000:

Dodman Point Cross   020°
St. Michael's Church Caerhays 348°
Gull Rk   300°

Plot it now (don't forget to enter it in your notebook first).

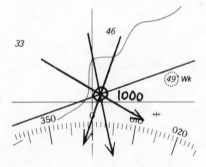

| 0938½ | 024° | 12 | ⅞ 071° |
| 1000 | 071° | 12 | Dodman Pt. Cross 020° St. Michael's Church 348° Gull Rk. 300° |

(Note that alterations of course and speed, go in the 'remarks' column of the note-book.)

If your fix is not within 0'·1 of this position rub it out and re-plot it.

You have just plotted two fixes from bearings that we have given you.

Of course, when you are on the bridge, you will have to select the marks and take the bearings yourself.

So, you must know what marks will provide you with a good fix.

The first rule is:

<u>There must be three or more marks.</u>

Look at these position lines

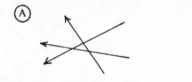

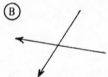

In both cases there was an error in the bearings.

Which set show it, A or B?

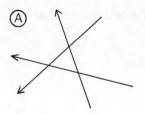

Ⓐ

Obviously two bearings, however much in error, will always cross in a point, so three or more marks are essential to be certain of a good fix.

The next rule: when you select from the chart the marks for your fix, <u>make sure that the marks are clearly charted, and that you will be able to see them.</u>

With this in mind, which of these marks would have been suitable for a fix at 0945?

St. Anthony's Head Lt (approximate bearing 261°)
Gerrans Church
Nare Head (approximate bearing 347°)
Dodman Point Cross

Gerrans Church
Dodman Point Cross

(St. Anthony's Hd Lt is obscured by the headland).

Although Nare Head has a spot height, and is quite steep, it has no clearly charted feature; Carne beacon or Gull Rock would be better.

Therefore, we are looking for three clearly charted marks that we will be able to see.

Now look at these position lines:

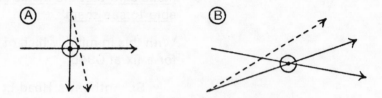

The firm lines show the bearings that were plotted. In both cases one bearing was in error by 5°, and the dotted lines show the correct bearing — that is, the one that should have been plotted.

On which fix was the position more in error?

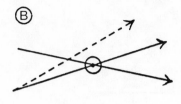

The narrower the angle of cut, the more effect an error in bearing will have on your position.

The rule is:

> <u>The angle of cut between any two marks must be *at least* 30°</u>
> (<u>but not more than 150°</u>).

What were the other two rules?

At least three marks.

Marks must be clearly charted and likely to be visible.

Now, another rule.

Look at these two bearings.

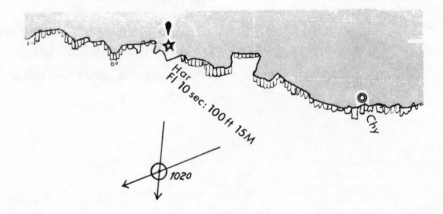

If either bearing was wrong, which would produce the greater error in position for a given error in the bearing, the light, or the chimney?

The chimney (because it is further away).

This rule then is:

Choose near marks in preference to far.

What are the four rules for choosing suitable marks for fixing?

There should be at least three marks.

The angle of cut must be at least 30°.

Marks must be clearly charted and likely to be visible.

Choose near marks in preference to far.

We said earlier on that if you plot three position lines you will be able to note a compass error if they do not cross in a point.

But there is a case, if you choose your marks badly, where the position lines will cross in a point even if there is a compass error.

Look at this diagram.

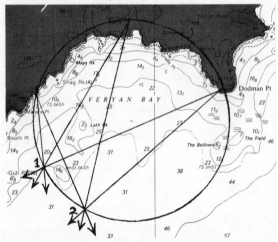

You fixed your position at 1, but your gyro was in error and your fix should have been at 2.

What rule about the choice of marks do we deduce from this situation? (Hint: consider what your position is in relation to the other marks.)

The rule:

<u>Not to choose marks with which you are on a common circumference.</u> (In your own words.)

Look at the diagram again to see why this is so.

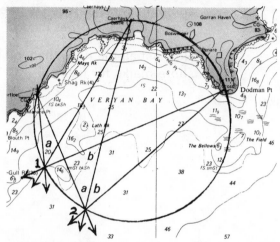

You will remember from your geometry that all the angles marked *a* are equal to each other and all the angles marked *b* are equal to each other, anywhere on the circumference of the circle.

As a gyro error will not change the angle *between* position lines, but only their direction, we could get position lines meeting in a point anywhere on this circle.

In position 50°11′·4N, 04°50′·3W would the following marks be suitable for fixing and why?

Dodman Point Cross
St. Michael's Church, Caerhays
Portloe CG Flagstaff

No

Because they are on a common circumference with the position.

(They are not precisely, but near enough to make them unreliable.)

A simple way to avoid choosing marks with which you are on a common circumference is to ensure that the centre mark is closer to you than the other marks.

Now list all the rules that you have learnt for choosing the correct shore marks for fixing.

There must be at least
3 marks.

The angle of cut must be
at least 30°.

Marks must be clearly
charted and likely to be
visible.

Select near marks in
preference to far.

Do not choose marks with
which you are on a common
circumference.

A final point about choosing fixing marks is the use of buoys.

At low water, buoys may not be in their charted positions

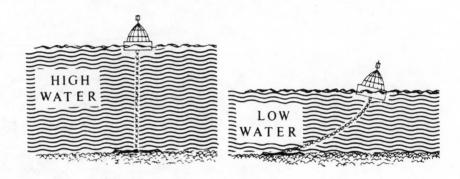

and, of course, their moorings may drag.

So, in general, buoys are/are not suitable for fixing marks. (Which?)

are not

While buoys are not suitable for fixing marks, nevertheless, they can be relied on for guidance when:

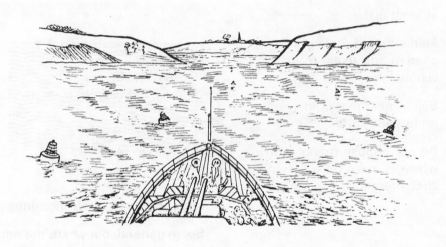

the ship's position is well established by other means,

or

the channel is liable to change from its charted position.

Look at the right-hand side of the chart for a moment.

If you were in position 50°15'N 04°10'W which of the following would be the best fixing marks?
(Don't forget to apply *all* the rules that you have learnt— look back to 49 if you cannot remember them.)

LHE Rame Hd
Breakwater Lt
BLDG (conspic.)
(behind the Mewstone)

Go to 52

Eddystone Lt
Breakwater Lt
BLDG (conspic.)

Go to 53

East Looe Lt
Breakwater Lt
CG LOOKOUT (conspic.)

Go to 54

LHE Rame Hd.
BLDG (conspic.)
CG LOOKOUT (conspic.)

Go to 55

You chose as best fixing marks:

LHE Rame Hd
Breakwater Lt
BLDG (conspic.)

If you put the point of your compass on a point 030°-0'·3 from the 40 metre sounding. Set the radius your position, and then describe a circle, you will find that the marks and your position lie nearly on its circumference.

You will remember from our diagram

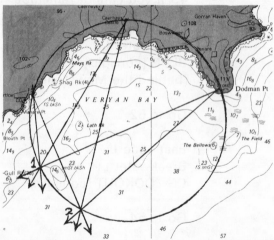

that if there was a gyro error we might plot the wrong position.

Your choice was not the best. Choose again.

Eddystone Lt	East Looe Lt	LHE Rame Hd
Breakwater Lt	Breakwater Lt	BLDG (conspic.)
BLDG (conspic.)	CG LOOKOUT	CG LOOKOUT
Go to 53	Go to 54	Go to 55

You chose as the best fixing marks:

Eddystone Lt
Breakwater Lt
BLDG (conspic.)

These marks are clearly charted, but the angle of cut between the Eddystone and the conspicuous building is less than 30° (they are on an almost reciprocal bearing).

Your choice was not the best, so choose again:

LHE Rame Head	East Looe Lt	LHE Rame Hd
Breakwater Lt	Breakwater Lt	BLDG (conspic.)
BLDG (conspic.)	CG LOOKOUT	CG LOOKOUT
Go to 52	Go to 54	Go to 55

You chose as best fixing marks:

East Looe Lt
Breakwater Lt
CG LOOKOUT (conspic.)

The marks are likely to be visible and clearly charted, the angle of cut is at least 30°, and you are not on a common circumference with them.

However East Looe Light is too distant when other objects are closer. As you should choose near objects, rather than far, in order to reduce the effect of any bearing or plotting error, you did not choose the best set of marks. Choose again.

LHE Rame Head	Eddystone Lt	LHE Rame Head
Breakwater Lt	Breakwater Lt	BLDG (conspic.)
BLDG (conspic.)	BLDG (conspic.)	CG LOOKOUT
Go to 52	Go to 53	Go to 55

You chose the best fixing marks:

LHE Rame Head
BLDG (conspic.)
CG LOOKOUT (conspic.)

The following characteristics are present in your choice of marks:

★ There are three marks.

★ The marks are clearly charted and are likely to be visible.

★ The angle of cut is more than 30°.

★ You are not on a common circumference with them.

★ The marks are not too distant.

So these are perfectly satisfactory marks for fixing — you chose correctly. Well done!

Go to 56.

In the last example we used the expression 'Left-Hand Edge'.

Because it is a very easily identified object, we often take visual bearings of an edge of land like this:

This is described as a right-hand/left-hand edge. (Which do you think?)

right-hand

If the edge of the land is to the right as you look at it from seaward, then it is a right-hand edge.

Is this a right-hand or left-hand edge?

left-hand

Would the end of Larmouth harbour jetty be a right-hand or left-hand edge to you at 0430?

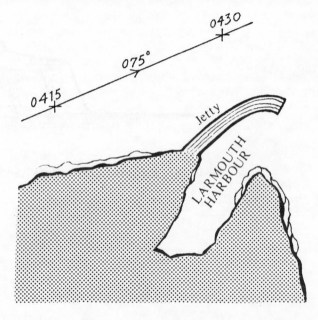

left-hand

You would see it like this:

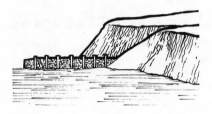

Now plan the next stages of your journey by plotting the following positions:

161° from Gribben Head 4·'5
                Daymark
165° from Polperro Lt - 1·'8
330° from Eddystone Lt - 4·'4

When you have plotted them, join them up, starting from your 1015 DR position.

Lay transparency 1 over your chart to check your plotting.

Return now to your journey.

It is now 1015 and you alter course to 052°.

Enter this in your notebook and DR on until 1045.

(To draw the DR ahead is usually referred to as to 'DR on' and we shall use this expression in the programme.)

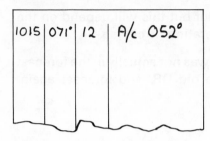

| 1015 | 071° | 12 | A/c 052° |

Lay transparency 2 over the chart to check your plotting.

By the time you have plotted a fix, it is already historical information — where the ship was at that time.

You must know where the ship is and where it is going to be; so whenever you plot a fix you must draw the_____ on from the fix.

DR

It is usual to DR on for about an hour but this will depend on the situation; it may be to the next alteration of course.

However, if a fix shows that the ship was not actually in the forecast DR position, you must rub out the old DR, and forecast again, starting at the fix.

If you plotted this fix.

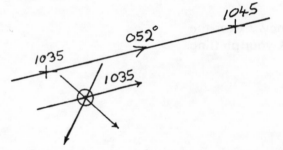

what should you do? (Assume that you are far from the nearest danger, and hence that the ship is quite safe.)

Re-plot the DR and draw it on for the next hour (or as needed) from the fix.

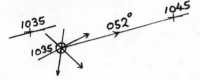

After taking a fix the same sequence must always be followed.

> Record in notebook.
> Plot fix.
> DR on for an hour (or as needed).

You must DR on from a fix so that your best estimate of the _____ and _____ positions of the ship are on the chart.

present
future

It is now 1045. You alter course to 057°, speed 10 knots.
DR on till 1115.

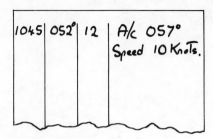

| 1045 | 052° | 12 | A/c 057°
Speed 10 Knots. |

Lay transparency 2 over chart to check your plotting.

If your positions are wrong, plot them again.

Why must you DR on from a fix?

★ DR positions at 1100 and 1115 to be marked on transparency 2.

To have your best estimate of the present and future positions of the ship on the chart. (Or your own words.)

You take the following fix at 1045.

LHE Dodman Pt 259°
Mevagissey Lt 287°
Gribben Hd 341°
Daymark

Plot this.

| 1045 | 057 | 10 | LHE Dodman
Pt 259°
Mevagissey
LT 287°
Gribben Hd
Daymark 341° |

Now, what must you do?

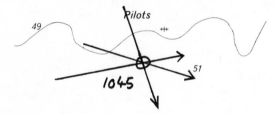

If your fix was not correct,
plot it again.

DR on

In this case DR on (using the course 057°, until the DR intersects the next course.

Then note the DR times every 15 minutes, and rub out the old DR.

Lay transparency 2 over the chart.

(If your positions are wrong, plot them again.)

Even when the gyro-compass is working correctly, it can have small errors from time to time, so we need a method of checking it.

Within sight of land, one method is to take a bearing of two objects that are in line with one another, and then see from the chart what the true bearing was.

The two objects in line are known as a <u>transit</u>.

Look at the chart. At about 1126 what objects could you see in transit? (There is a marking on the chart here which will help you.)

Measured mile beacons at
Talland Bay

This transit has the bearing already written on the chart, but you can select your own objects, and measure the bearing with a parallel ruler, if the objects are clearly charted.

Look at the chart again. If you had wanted to check your compass at about 1017 what objects would have provided a transit, and what would have been their bearing from you?

LHE Dodman Pt
St. Michael's Church
Caerhays (308°)

You may have chosen two other objects but these are the clearest—the two marks are on the same level, two edges of land are easy to identify and if they are steep it will be easy to note when they are in line.

Remember, you need an accurate bearing, so choose marks with _____edges, or marks which are themselves_____, so that you can observe the exact moment of transit.

vertical

vertical

(You may have said 'steep', or a similar word.)

There are some other points about choosing marks for a transit. For instance, to check your gyro at about 1045, why would you not choose Tywardreath Church and Gribben Hd daymark from the chart?

The church would be
obscured behind the land.

To summarise so far, the two marks for a transit must be:

1. Clearly charted with_____edges.
2. Both must be_____at the time of transit.

vertical

visible

Look at this diagram.

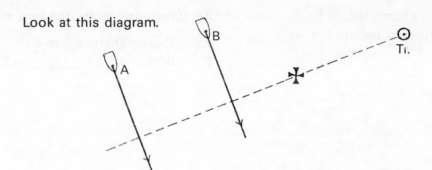

Both observers have the same distance to go until the marks are in transit, but observer A sees this:

and observer B sees this:

So, to observer B, the angle between the marks is changing more quickly/slowly than to observer A. (Which?)

To observer B, the angle between the marks is changing *more quickly.*

Look at the diagram again.

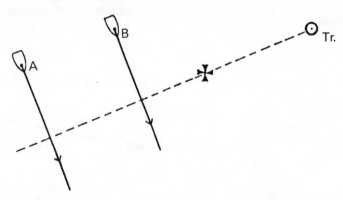

The rate at which the angle between the marks will change, depends on how close the observer is to the front mark, and the distance from the front mark to the back mark.

Think about this, and then confirm it from the diagram.

The 'rule-of-thumb' is that the distance from the_____ _____to the _____ _____ should be not less than ⅓ of the distance from the observer to the front mark.

front mark

back mark

The more rapidly the angle between the marks closes, the more accurately the observer can note the exact moment of transit.

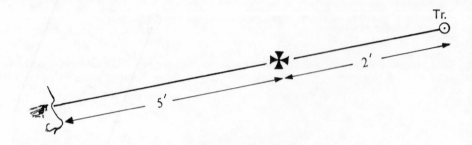

The distance from the church to the tower is not less than _____ of the distance from the church to the observer.

⅓

When the angle between the marks alters quickly, the transit is called 'sensitive'.

What is the rule for choosing marks that will give an adequately sensitive transit for checking the gyro?

The distance from front mark to back mark must be at least ⅓ of the distance from the front mark to the observer.

One further point about transits.

When you write in your notebook that one object is in transit with another, you write it like this:

0933 LHE Zone Pt Ø FS Pendennis Castle 285½°.

Go back to about 1025 and assume that you take the transit of RHE Chapel Pt and Mevagissey Lt.

Read it off and enter it correctly in your notebook.

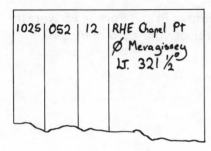

At about 1031 you wish to check the gyro-compass.

Choose the best transit.

LHE Dodman Pt
Ø Portloe FS is best

If the bearing that you took when Dodman Pt and Portloe FS were in transit was 270°, what was the error of your gyro compass?

Nil

This fact should also be entered in your notebook.
(The time of taking the transit was 1031.)

Do this now.

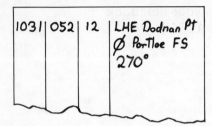

Are you remembering to head correctly each new page of your notebook?

What are the rules for choosing suitable marks for a transit?

Marks must be clearly charted.

Marks must have vertical edges, or be themselves vertical.

The distance from front to back mark must be at least ⅓ of the distance from front mark to the observer.

When selecting marks for a fix you may see some conspicuous object, and not be able to identify it on the chart.

One way to identify it is to 'shoot it up'.

This is how it is done.

At 1100 you take this fix:

Mevagissey Lt	273°
Gribben Head Daymark	312½°
Polperro Lt.	031°

and at the same time you take a bearing of a small island that you want to identify at 047°.

Plot the fix first.

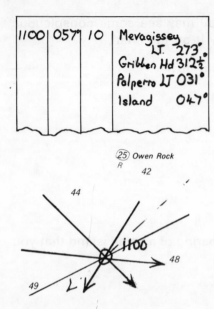

| 1100 | 057° | 10 | Mevagissey LT. 273°
Gribben Hd 312½°
Polperro LT 031°
Island 047° |

25 Owen Rock
R
42

If your fix was not correct,
plot it again.

Having plotted your fix, plot the bearing of 047° from the fix, extending it over the coast.

What is the island?

St. George's Island

This method of identifying an object is called, as we said earlier, 'shooting up'.

The other way of identification is to wait until the unidentified object is in transit with a known object, as in this picture.

Now draw the bearing on the chart, and see what object it passes through.

At about 1116 you note that a church spire is in transit with Shag Rock, bearing 323°.

What church is this?

Lansallos Church

Before we go on with our journey, some revision questions.

What is the definition of DR?

Course and speed through the water.

What *must* you do when you take a fix that does not fall exactly on the DR position?

DR on from the fix for one hour, (or as the situation demands).

What rules must you apply when choosing marks to provide a reliable fix?

Marks must be clearly charted and likely to be visible.

There must be 3 or more marks.

The angle of cut must be at least 30°.

Near marks must be chosen in preference to far.

You must not be on a common circumference with the marks.

Now, back to our journey.

Assuming that you continue at a speed of 10 knots, when (to the nearest minute) should you alter to 117°?

1124
(from your 1115 position
you have to steam 1'·5,
which is 9 minutes at
10 knots).

You take the following fix at 1115.

Gribben Hd Daymark	289°
Polperro Lt	008°
LHE St. George's Island	040°

Plot the fix.

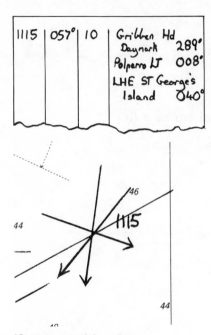

It is now 1124, you alter course to 117°.

If your position is not correct, plot it again.

Remember, you must always mark fixes with a small neat ☉ and a four-figure time.

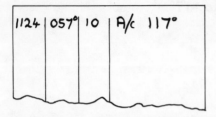

`1124 | 057° | 10 | A/c 117°`

Lay transparency 3 over your chart.

Plot your course again if you are wrong.

You take this fix at 1130.

LHE St. George's Island	009°
RHE Rame Head	081°
Eddystone Lt	128°

Plot the bearings but do not mark them as a fix.

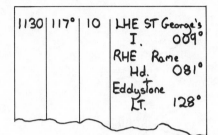

| 1130 | 117° | 10 | LHE ST George's I. 009° RHE Rame Hd. 081° Eddystone LT. 128° |

These position lines have resulted in what is called a 'cocked hat', that is, they have not cut at one point but have formed a triangle.

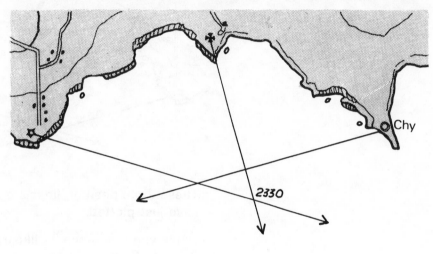

Your plot should look like this:

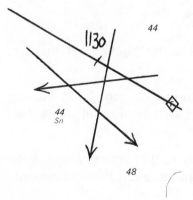

Look again at this illustration.

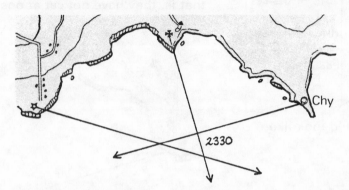

These three position lines are similar to the 'cocked hat' that you have just plotted.

When you saw a similar illustration to this on page 34 it showed three position lines crossing in a point, so that you could mark their intersection as a fix.

Do you think that you could be equally sure of your position when the position lines do not cross in a point, as in the illustration?

We asked what you thought — you should have answered 'no'; because as the three position lines do not cross in a point, your position is not clearly defined in relation to the three objects.

Look again at the illustration.

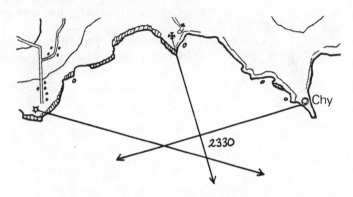

The ship could not have been *simultaneously* on all three position lines at 2330. You now have to decide whether you have enough indication of the ship's position to mark a fix on the chart.

Before deciding on this, you should see whether you have made a mistake, so_____ your plotting.

check

If, after checking your plotting, you still have a cocked hat, then you should consider whether you observed the bearings correctly.

You obviously can't take exactly the same bearings again, as the ship has moved on, so what should you do?

Take the fix again, using the same marks. (Or your own words.)

So, if you have a cocked hat — check your_____ ,

if you still have a cocked hat, take the fix again.

plotting

If, after you have taken and plotted the fix again, you still have a cocked hat, you should then decide whether to mark a fix on the chart. A rule-of-thumb guide is that: provided the cocked hat is a small one, you can mark the centre of it as a fix, and the ship's position will not be very far in error.

Do you consider that you could mark as a fix the centre of the cocked hat that you have just plotted?

Yes

(The cocked hat measures only about 0'3 across at its widest part, and you had a good fix at 1115, so your 1130 position will probably not be far from the 1130 DR.)

When you can mark the cocked hat as a fix is a matter of experience, depending upon the scale of the chart, the reliability of the chart and compass, and your nearness to dangers; but the important things to consider are:

★ your confidence in the ship's position,

★ the size of the cocked hat compared with your distance from the nearest danger,

★ the fact that your true position could be outside the cocked hat.

However, before you decide whether to mark the cocked hat as a fix, what will you have done to try and get rid of it?

Checked your plotting.

(If you still then had a cocked hat, take the fix again.)

You take this fix at 1140:

LHE St. George's Island	342°
RHE Rame Hd	074°
Eddystone Lt	130°

Plot these bearings.

What should you do now?

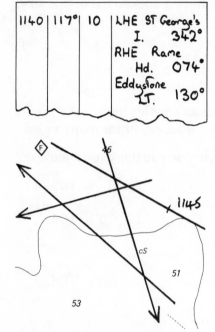

1140	117°	10	LHE ST George's I. 342° RHE Rame Hd. 074° Eddystone LT. 130°

You should have obtained a cocked hat about 0.5 by 1.0. If you didn't, check your plotting again.

Check your plotting.

If a cocked hat is still apparent, take the fix again.

If, after taking the fix again, you still have a cocked hat of this size, the trouble might be:

Gyro error.
Wrongly identified marks.
Poorly charted marks.

The first two are the most likely— marks are only likely to be poorly charted in areas which have not been surveyed for many years.

If you still have a large cocked hat, what do you think you should do:

Mark the centre as a fix?	Go to 103.
Take it as a danger warning and check all navigation?	Go to 104.
Apply the same error to all bearings until position lines cross in a point?	Go to 105.

You say that you would mark the centre of the cocked hat as a fix.

This action would be wrong (and possibly dangerous) because:

You do not know what has caused the error— hence you do not know that the real position of the ship is anywhere inside the cocked hat.

Secondly, even if the cause were to be a gyro error of equal amount on all bearings, the position of the ship could still be outside the cocked hat.

Try again — would you:

Take it as a danger warning, and check all navigation?   Go to 104.

Apply the same error to all bearings, until they cross in a point?   Go to 105.

You say that you would take a large cocked hat to be a danger warning and check all navigation.

A large cocked hat is a clear indication that something is amiss, either with the compass, or with your identification of the marks that you are observing.

If your compass has a large error, or you have wrongly identified a mark, you may have been steering in the wrong direction, or some of your recent fixes may have been wrong.

So your position may not be where you think it is, and you should certainly check all your past navigation.

If you chose this answer first time, well done!

Go to 106.

You say you would apply the same error to all bearings until position lines cross in a point.

If you found that applying the same error to all bearings gave a fix, you might use this as an indication of a gyro error, but you should not use it as a fix.

Doing this is known as 'fiddling it to fit' and if the crossing in a point was not due to gyro error, but was pure chance, then you may put yourself in the dangerous position of relying on a fix which isn't one.

Choose again — would you:

Mark the centre as a fix?   Go to 103.

Take it as a danger warning, and
check all navigation?   Go to 104.

Chapter 3

We will assume that you have now checked all your previous navigation and decide that the fix at 1115 is quite reliable, but your fixing since then is suspect, so your DR position may not be quite correct.

However, you are satisfied that your gyro is accurate.

At 1207 you alter course to 090° and the visibility closes down, so you reduce speed to 8 knots.

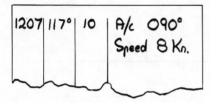

| 1207 | 117° | 10 | A/c 090°
Speed 8 Kn. |

Because of the reduced visibility, the only fixing mark you can see is Eddystone Lighthouse.

At 1210 you take a bearing of Eddystone Lt. 155°.

Plot this.

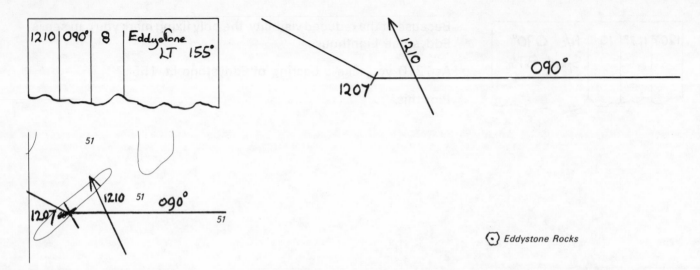

1210	090°	8	Eddystone LT 155°

Eddystone Rocks

At 1210 you must have been somewhere on the position line that you have just taken — though you do not know where for certain.

Therefore, you should DR on from the position line (it is convenient to DR on along the course already drawn, although you are not necessarily on that line).

DR on until 1225.

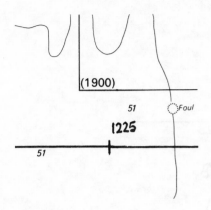

(1900)

51   ⟨⟩Foul

1225

51

The insert shows your new
1225 DR position.

If you did not rub out the
old DR, do it now.

At 1225 you still have only Eddystone visible, and at this time you
take a bearing of Eddystone Lt 185°.

Plot this.

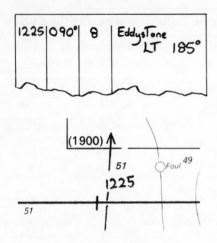

If this position line is not correct, plot it again.

Look at this diagram.

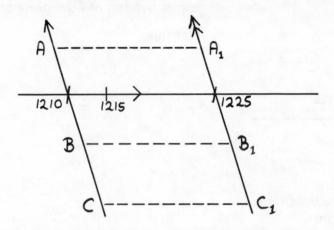

If, at 1210, you were anywhere on the position line (say at A, B or C) then at 1225 you would have been anywhere on a line parallel to the 1210 position line, passing through the 1225 DR (say at A1, B1 or C1).

Draw this line through the 1225 position and mark it with two arrows at the end, like this ⟨⟨———.

The position line that you have just drawn through the 1225 DR is called a <u>transferred</u> position line, because you have just transferred it from 1210.

Now extend the transferred position line and the 1225 bearing until they cut.

Have we now obtained a fix?

Yes.   Go to 112.

No.   Go to 113.

You say:

Yes, we have obtained a fix.

Since we are somewhere on the 1225 <u>transferred</u> position line and we must also be somewhere on the $\overline{1225}$ position line (of 185°) then their point of intersection must be our position. So you are right.

This is called a 'running fix'.

Mark the intersection of the position lines as a fix for 1225.

Go to 114.

You say:

No, we have not obtained a fix.

Since we are somewhere on the 1225 <u>transferred</u> position line and we must also be somewhere on the 1225 position line (of 185°) then their point of intersection must be our position, and this is called a 'running fix' so we *have* obtained a fix.

But if you thought that we had not got a fix because we only had two position lines and that its accuracy depends on the accuracy of your estimate of the ship's run between the two position lines, then you have a good point, and have realised that a running fix is not so reliable as an ordinary fix, and we would not use it if better methods of fixing were available.

If you thought this, your answer is right.

Mark the intersection of the two position lines as a fix for 1225.

Go to 116.

Although we have taken a running fix, we cannot place the same reliance on it as a 3-bearing fix.

Why do you think this is?

There are only two position lines, and the accuracy of the fix depends on whether the ship has made good the DR course and speed between the two position lines.

So although we call this a running <u>fix</u>, we would not use it if better methods of fixing were available.

Go to 116.

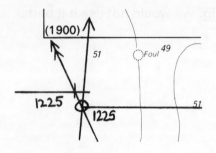

If your fix was not accurate, plot it again.

Remember, the accuracy of a running fix depends on whether the ship has made good exactly the DR course and speed between position lines. We shall come back to this later, when we consider how to estimate the ship's run more accurately.

At 1230 you alter course to 135° to investigate the report of a ship in distress, 5 miles South East of Eddystone Rocks.

The visibility is still poor, but you increase speed to 12 knots.

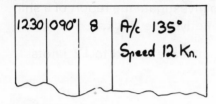

| 1230 | 090° | 8 | A/c 135° Speed 12 Kn. |

Lay transparency 3 over your chart.

If your plotting was not accurate, plot the DR again.

As the visibility is still low, you decide to fix by radar.

When fixing by radar you will use <u>range</u> only, and not bearing; so you are looking for two or more objects to give you a good range.

Look at these pictures:

Which coastline do you think will give you a better radar echo, A or B?

B

(Because the beam is reflected back at right angles — or nearly so.)

You look therefore for a vertical or steep cliff face, or any object rising sheer out of the water.

(We have over-simplified this point — you will no doubt find out more about radar reflection in due course, but for the purposes of this programme we hope you will accept what we say!)

In Whitesand Bay what part of the coast would be *least* suitable for radar fixing?

The coast between
Seaton and Downderry.

To the North of your position, which of the following would be suitable for Radar fixing?

Rame Head
Mewstone
Yealm Head

All of them.

Some of the rules for selecting visual fixing marks also apply to the selection of radar marks (though not always for the same reasons).

A radar display is a circular screen of a fixed physical size.

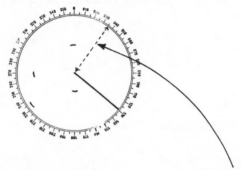

Your ship is at the centre, and the radius can be made to represent various ranges.

If the radius represented 1 mile, you could measure range more accurately/less accurately than if it represented 10 miles. (Say which.)

If the range represented
1 mile you could measure
range <u>more accurately</u> than
if it represented 10 miles.

(If the display was 10
inches in diameter, on a
1 mile scale 1 inch would
represent 200 yards; while
on a 10 mile scale 1 inch
would only represent
1 mile.)

Therefore, you should choose near objects in preference to far, as
you can measure their range more accurately.

Which would be the better mark for radar fixing at 1230?

Rame Head or St. George's Island

Rame Head
(It is nearer to your
position.)

So we need steep marks, as close to the ship as possible.

Now look at this diagram.

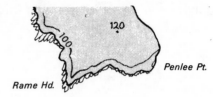

The position lines are arcs of range circles from the two marks.

Do you think this gives a good fix? If not, why not?

No

The angle of cut is poor, and there are only two marks.

So we must consider angle of cut and the number of marks in the same way as we do for visual marks.

Bearing this in mind, choose suitable marks for a radar fix at 1245.

Any three that are:

1. Steep.

2. Have an angle of cut of at least 30°.

(Rame Hd, Mewstone are good ones, but Eddystone will give us a poor cut with Mewstone so we use Plymouth Breakwater and Yealm Hd instead.)

At 1240 you take radar ranges as follows:

Rame Hd.   5:7
Breakwater   7:2
Yealm Hd.   7:15

Plot the fix by describing arcs with your compasses. Then arrow the position lines at both ends and mark as a fix, like this:

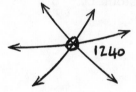

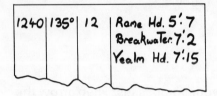

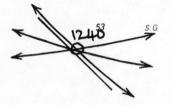

If your fix is not accurate,
plot it again.

We repeat that there is more to selecting radar fixing marks than this – you must, for instance, be familiar with the capabilities of your equipment – but these are the basic points.

You take this fix at 1250:

Rame Head	7:1
Mewstone	7:0
Eddystone Lt.	3:7

Plot this.

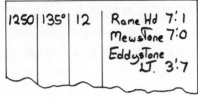

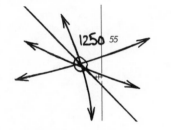

If your fix is wrong, plot it again.

A radar range can of course be used with a visual bearing. Like this:

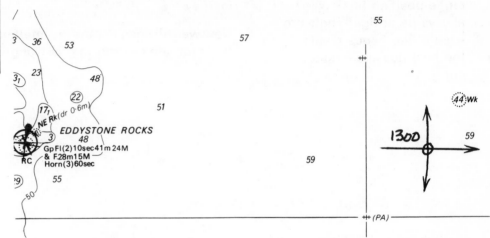

We would, of course, always need a third position line for a reliable fix. If, however, a third position line is not available, and if we use the mark for both range and bearing we will get the most accurate fix possible from one mark.

Why? (Remember one of your rules for choosing good marks for fixing.)

Because the bearing and range position lines will always be at right-angles to each other, hence giving the best possible angle of cut.

We will be using visual bearings and radar ranges later in our journey.

Now we will consider the last method of fixing that you will learn in this programme, and that is fixing by Decca.

The Decca Navigator is a method of radio fixing which extends all round the coast of the British Isles, and is also available in many other parts of the world.

A fix is taken by taking readings from dials; these readings correspond to the lattice lines which are over-printed on all charts which have the prefix L(D).

Equipment now available computes Latitude and Longitude without the need to plot Decca readings.

Has the number of your chart got this prefix?

Yes
(L(D1)5050)
No
Only 5050
(If you do not need to
practice Decca plotting
go to 135.)

On a navigational chart the lattice lines (which are printed over the whole sea area) are printed in colour.

There are three colours— Red, Green and Purple— and the lines may run in any direction.

On the chart we are using Red, Green and Purple are printed. It happens that Red runs approximately from east to west, Green approximately from north to south and Purple approximately from north east to south west.

Passing through your 1230 position (016° Eddystone 3˙8) there is a thick red line.

What is the marking on this line?

A.6   What is the nearest Green line to the West of your 1240 position?
(048° Eddystone Lt. 3:3)

C.38

It just happens that on this chart Red runs approximately east and west, and Green approximately north and south.

On other charts this will always/may not always be the same. (Which?)

may not always

(It will depend where the
Decca stations are.)

To plot a Decca fix, you interpolate between the lines.

It does not matter which colour you plot first.

Plot this fix at 1300:

    Red   A.10

    Green   C.33

Indicate that this is a Decca fix by drawing two lines, one parallel to
the Red lattice lines, and the other to the Green lattice lines,
through the position, like this:

1300

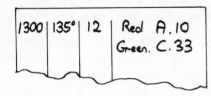

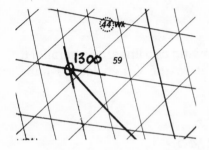

(If you remembered the notebook, well done.)

(Don't forget to DR on from the fix.)

Now plot this Decca fix at 1315.

Red   A.14·4

Green   B.46·6

For this fix you will have to interpolate between the lattice lines. (If you do not have an interpolator, use your dividers and the latitude scale, to make the interpolation.)

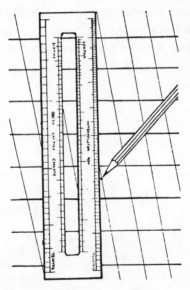

Take your Decca interpolator and put it on the chart so that a graduation of <u>ten</u> units corresponds exactly with lattice lines Red A.14 and Red A.15. Mark the position of A.14·4 with a dot. Then rule a line through the dot, parallel to the Red lattice lines.

Now repeat the procedure to plot Green 46·6, ruling a line to intersect the Red A.14·4 reading.

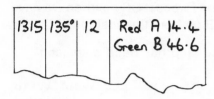

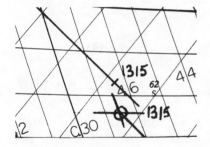

DR on from the fix if you have not done so.

Chapter 4

It is now 1330 and you hear that the report of the ship in distress has been cancelled.

You are told that you will be proceeding on course 340°, speed 10 knots, from 1335.

Plot the course.

(Your position at 1330 is:

50° 06′·15N 04° 02′·4W).

Use chart 5050 if you are not plotting Decca fixes.

Lay transparency 4 over the chart.

If your plot is wrong, change it.

So far, if the ship has not been in the forecast DR position we have accepted the fact and drawn the DR on from the position of the fix.

We now need to consider why the ship has been displaced.

It may be due to LEEWAY.

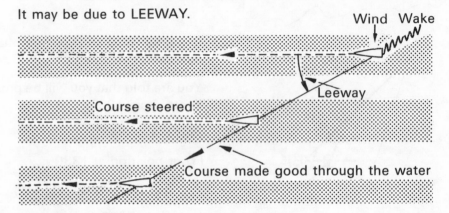

Leeway is the amount, usually expressed in degrees, that the ship is set off her course due to the effect of the_____.

wind

Leeway is difficult to forecast as, without experience, it is difficult to say how much any ship will be, so to speak, pushed sideways through the water. Therefore, we will not consider its effect any more in this programme.

However, the effect of the movement of the water mass itself is easy to forecast, as the ship will be carried along with the water movement. The type of water movement that we will consider is TIDAL STREAM.

If the tidal stream was flowing in a direction of 210° at a speed of 1 knot, and your ship was stopped, how far, and in what direction, would the ship move in one hour?

1 mile in a direction of 210°

If the water is moving, then of course the ship must move with it, at exactly the same rate.

Now let us consider what happens when the ship is moving through the water as well.

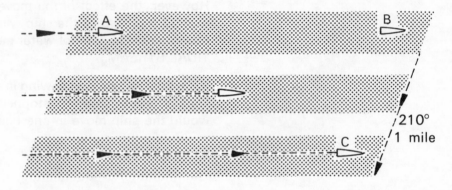

If the ship is steering 090° and the water itself is moving in a direction of 210° at a speed of 1 knot, where will the ship be after one hour, at B or at C?

At C

(Because the ship will have
been carried down steadily
in a 210° direction since
leaving position A.)

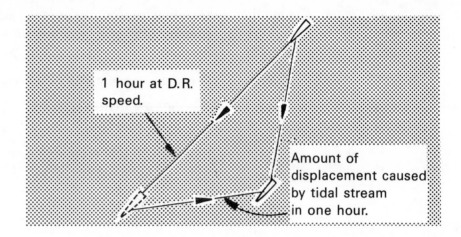

1 hour at D.R.
speed.

Amount of
displacement caused
by tidal stream
in one hour.

So the ship will always move with the tidal stream (in whatever
direction it is flowing) and, provided you can forecast what the
speed and direction of the tidal stream are expected to be, you can
estimate how much the ship will be displaced.

If you estimate the amount that the ship has been displaced for the
period of time since your last fix and then apply this displacement to
the DR position, you will obtain your E_____ Position.

Estimated

There are other factors as well as leeway and tidal stream that you should take into account when working out your Estimated Position.

These are movements of the water such as:

OCEAN CURRENTS and
SURFACE DRIFT.

However, as this programme deals only with basic chartwork, we will only consider the effect of TIDAL STREAM.

The Estimated Position (E.P. for short) is marked like this:

$\triangle$ 1520.

When you see this symbol in this programme, what will you know has been applied to the DR position?

tidal stream

What does E.P. stand for?

Estimated Position

We shall now go on to the method of plotting the Estimated Position, using tidal stream.

At 1335 you take this fix, alter course to 340° and reduce to 10 knots:

    Eddystone Lt.   300°
    Radar range   10:8

Plot this fix.

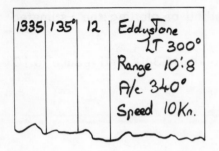

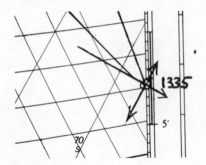

At 1350 you take the following Decca fix:

Red	A15·6	OR	50° 07:75N
Green	B43·0		04° 03:4 W

Plot the 1350 DR and then fix your position (but <u>do not</u> DR ahead from this fix, you will see why in a moment).

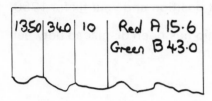

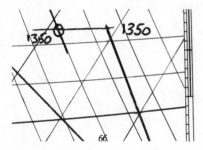

Leeway has been negligible since 1335.

What could account for the difference between your 1350 fix and your 1350 DR?

(Remember, we are only considering one type of water movement in this programme.)

Are you marking all fixes with the proper symbol and a time? This is very important.

tidal stream

Now draw a line between your DR position and your fix for 1350.

This shows the amount that the ship has been displaced between 1335 and 1350 by the tidal stream.

How long is this line (in miles)?

0:5

The ship has been displaced 0:5 in fifteen minutes, so you can now calculate the amount of displacement in one hour.

This will give you the rate (that is, the speed) of the tidal stream in knots.

What, then, is the rate of the tidal stream?

2· knots   Now measure the set (that is, the direction) of the tidal stream.

Set of the tidal stream is 270°

(<u>Not</u> 090°. Set is measured in the direction that the tidal stream is flowing.)

We can say, therefore, that the set of the tidal stream is 270° rate 2· knots.

A line which shows the magnitude and direction of a force is called a VECTOR.

The line that you have just measured to determine tidal stream is called the _____ _____ _____ .

tidal stream vector

The tidal stream vector is always marked with three arrows, like this:

Mark the vector that you have just drawn.

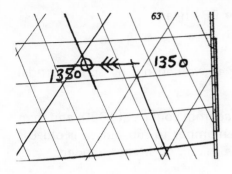

You know that when the fix does not fall on the DR, you must always DR ahead so that the present and future positions of the ship are always on the chart.

But when the ship has been affected by tidal stream, you will not plot a new DR position – simply because DR position does not take into account tidal stream and so will not be the accurate position of the ship.

We call the position that takes into account tidal stream, the _____ _____.

Estimated Position

The next thing to do is plot your EP ahead.

You will do this for 1405.

Remember that we said that EP is worked out by applying tidal stream to the DR position.

So first of all draw in the DR course from your fix at 1350, and then plot a DR position for 1405. Remember to rub out your old DR course and position for 1405, as this is no longer needed.

Do this now.

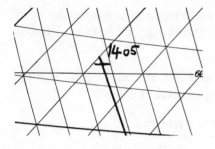

If you did not get the DR
position right, plot it again.

You will now have to draw the tidal stream vector from the DR
position for 1405 — remember the set of the tidal stream is 270°,
rate 2·0 knots.

How long will the tidal stream vector be?

0·5   Go to 154
1·0   Go to 155
2·0   Go to 156
I'm not sure — Go to 157.

You say that you would draw in the tidal stream vector, length 0·5

In order to plot the EP for 1405 you will need to know the amount that the ship will be displaced by tidal stream from 1350, an interval of fifteen minutes.

You would, therefore, draw in the tidal stream vector for 15 minutes. Its length will be 0·5 — so you were correct.

Now plot the EP for 1405, using the symbol △

When you have done this, go to page 158.

You say that you would draw in the tidal stream vector, length 1:0

This is the amount that the ship will be displaced in half an hour.

But in order to plot the EP for 1405, you will need to know the amount that the ship will be displaced between 1350 and 1405, an interval of 15 minutes.

So you must draw in the tidal stream vector for 15 minutes. Its length will be 0·5 — so you were wrong.

Now plot the EP for 1405 using the symbol △ .

Then go to page 158.

You say that you would draw in the tidal stream vector, length 2·0

This is the amount that the ship will be displaced in an hour.

But in order to plot the EP for 1405, you will need to know the amount that the ship will be displaced between 1350 and 1405, an interval of fifteen minutes.

So you must draw the tidal stream vector for fifteen minutes. Its length will be 0·5 — so you were wrong.

Now plot the EP for 1405, using the symbol △

Then go to page 158.

You say that you aren't sure how long the tidal stream vector will be to plot EP for 1405

You have already measured the amount that the ship was displaced by tidal stream between 1335 and 1350, a time interval of fifteen minutes. In order to plot the EP for 1405 you need to know the amount that the ship will be displaced between 1350 and 1405 also an interval of fifteen minutes.

You calculated the rate of the tidal stream as 2·0 knots. Therefore, the length of the tidal stream vector must be a quarter of this, 0·5.

Now plot your EP for 1405, using the symbol △

Then go to page 158.

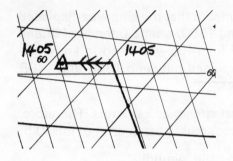

If you did not get this right,
plot the EP again.

Now draw a line through your fix at 1350 and your EP for 1405.

This line shows the ship's course, taking into account displacement by tidal stream. It represents the ship's actual course in relation to the earth's surface (called 'the ground').

This line is called the TRACK; mark it with the correct symbol, like this ——≪——.

Lay transparency 4 over the chart.

The track shows the actual course and speed MADE GOOD OVER THE_____ .

GROUND

By measuring the track, you can determine actual course and speed made good over the ground between 1335 and 1405.

Do this now.

Course 330°

Speed 10·6 knots

Define track.

The track is the actual course and speed made good over the ground.

The time is now 1400. At 1405 you are to proceed on course 260°, speed 12.

Tidal stream will be 120°, 1·2 knots.

Plot your EP for 1420.

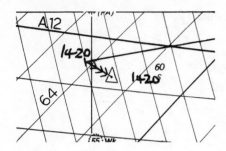

Draw in the track between 1405 and 1420.

What will be the course and speed made good?

If your position was not correct, plot it again.

Course 256°

Speed 11·2 knots

At 1405 you set course 260°, speed 12, as planned.

Your position by Decca is:

Red	A10·8	OR	50° 10:05N
Green	B44·8		04° 05:6W

Plot this.

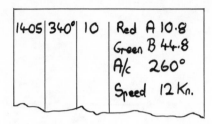

1405	340°	10	Red A 10.8
			Green B 44.8
			A/c 260°
			Speed 12 Kn.

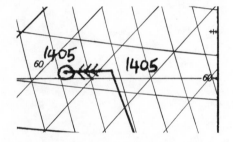

If you did not get this,
plot the position again.

The time is now 1415.

You are told to go to position 'A':

50° 07.0N

04° 30.0W

from your EP at 1420.

You will reduce speed to 6 knots at 1420 as visibility is again closing in.

First of all plot position 'A'. You will find that the ruler isn't long enough to reach the latitude scale.

What should you do?

Use the ruler for marking longitude and the dividers for latitude.

Here is the position again:

50° 07:0N

04° 30:0W.

Plot the position.

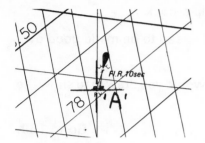

If your position is not correct, plot it again.

You estimate that tidal stream will remain steady at 120°, 1·2 knots.

You will remember that in order to work out your EP for 1405, you forecast your 1405 DR position and then applied tidal stream to it to determine how far you were displaced.

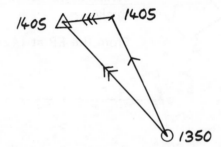

But you now want to know what course to steer, taking into account the fact that in one hour the ship will be displaced a distance of 1·2 miles in a direction of 120° from that course.

So the first step is to draw in the tidal stream vector for one hour from your EP at 1420.

This will give you the amount of displacement that you will have to allow for in one hour, when you set a course to pass through position 'A'.

Draw in the Tidal Stream Vector (TSV).

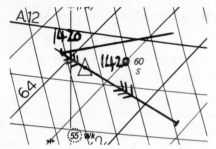

The next stage is to draw in the ship's track.

This will show the actual course and speed to be made good over the ground.

Which of the two lines shown below would you draw in to show the track?

From the EP at 1420 to position 'A' . . . . Go to 169.

If you did not get this right, plot it again.

From the end of the tidal stream vector to position 'A' . . . . Go to 170.

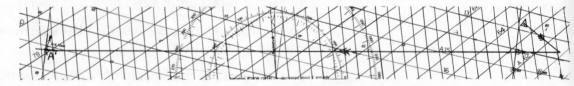

You say that you would draw in the track from your EP for 1420 to position 'A'.

The track must always join your actual position to your future position — because this will be the <u>track</u> the ship follows.

So you were right.

Draw in the track, using the correct symbol.

Then go to page 171.

1420

Posn. 'A'

You say that you would draw in the track from the end of the tidal stream vector to position 'A'.

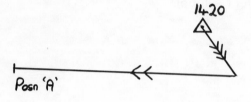

The track shows the actual course and speed to be made good, therefore you must draw a line between your PRESENT POSITION and POSITION TO PASS THROUGH, because this will be the track of the ship.

So this time you were wrong.

Draw in the track from the 1420 EP using the correct symbol.

Then go to page 171.

What is the course to be made good between the 1420 EP and position 'A'?

260°

Now you must find out by construction what course you must steer to compensate for the effect of the tidal stream.

Pick up your compasses and with centre the end of the tidal stream vector, and radius your speed, describe an arc to cut the track. (Remember, your speed will be 6 knots.)

Do this now.

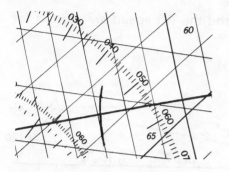

The arc should cut the track in the position shown above, if it does not, plot it again.

Now join the end of the tidal stream vector to the point where the arc and the track intersect.

This line gives you the course to steer to make good a course of 260°.

Measure the course to steer.

The course to steer is 267°.

If you did not get this right, measure it again.

On the chart, the tidal stream and the DR speed are plotted for one hour.

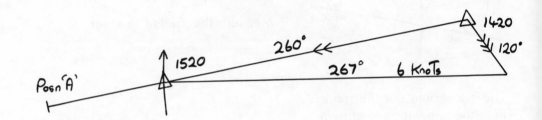

The length of the third side of the triangle (that is, the distance along the track from the 1420 EP to the point where the arc cuts the track) will, therefore, give you the speed made good for one hour.

Measure from the chart the speed made good.

5 knots

You have just drawn the triangle to find out what course to steer to make good a track of 260°.

This is sometimes a little difficult to grasp, so let us look at it more closely.

At 1420 you estimate that you will be in the 1420 Estimated Position and steering 267°, thus:

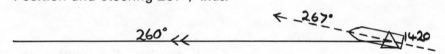

At 1520 you will be in the 1520 Estimated Position.

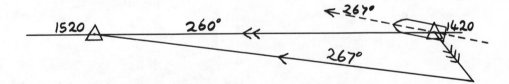

What will you be steering?

267°

So you will have moved from the 1420 to the 1520 EP, steering 267°, but in a direction (i.e. making good) 260°, thus:

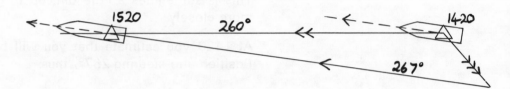

If we draw the triangle for half an hour, (halving all values of course), this would be the picture:

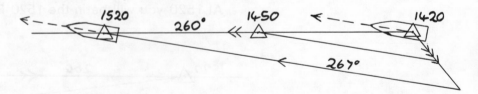

What position would you be in at 1450 and what would you be steering?

In the 1450 EP, and steering 267°.

At 1450 therefore, you will still be steering 267°, and moving in a direction over the ground (making good) 260°.

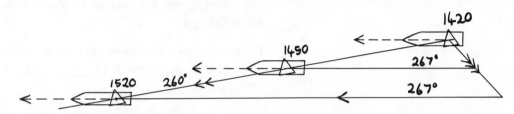

If we draw the triangle for *any* period of time, the result will still be the same.

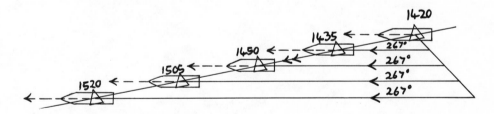

Provided the tidal stream stays the same, will the ship remain on the track of 260° after 1520?

Yes

It doesn't matter for what period you draw the triangle; you can draw it for more than an hour as well as for less, and the result will always be the same — given the same tidal stream and other factors.

To a celestial observer, the ship would appear to be moving crabwise along a track of____ , but with its bow pointing in a direction of____.

260°
267°

The time is now 1450 and you have received a revised position 'A' as follows:-

50° 08ʹ15N
04° 20ʹ0W

The distance from your EP at 1420 to <u>new</u> position 'A' is 6ʹ75 miles.

At what time will you reach new position 'A'?

1541
(The time to steam 6·75
miles at the speed made
good, that is 5 knots,

is $\dfrac{6·75}{5}$ x 60 mins

= 81 minutes)

Now plot your EP along the track every quarter of an hour, starting from 1430.

Notes

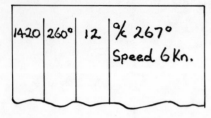

1420	260°	12	% 267°
			Speed 6 Kn.

At 1504 your position by Decca is:-

Red   A 14·6   50° 08·7 N
Green C 46·7   or   04° 15·3 W

Plot this.

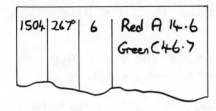

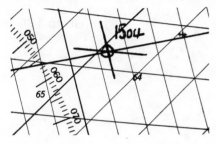

From new position 'A' you are to set course and speed to rendezvous in position:

50° 12'0N

04° 25'1W

at 1611.

Draw in the track between new position 'A' and the rendezvous position.

What will be the course and speed that you will need to make good?

Course is 320°, speed 10·1 knots.

If you did not get the right answer, plot the position again.

Remember to mark off your position along the track every quarter of an hour from 1545.

These positions will show the course and speed that you expect to make good along the track so will these be your:

DR positions for 1545 and 1600 Go to 185.

EP's for 1545 and 1600 Go to 186.

You say that you will call the positions - the DR positions for 1545 and 1600

You will remember that we defined DR as course and speed through the water. Track was defined as course and speed over the ground, that is, the movement of the ship relative to the earth's surface.

So any point along the track must be the EP at that time, as it is your best estimate of the ship's position taking into account everything that will affect it.

Hence the positions on the track for 1545 and 1600 are the EP's for 1545 and 1600 — so this time you were wrong.

Plot them now on the chart, if you have not already done so.

Then go to 187.

You say that these will be EP's for 1545 and 1600

You will remember that our definitions of EP and track took into account the mass movement of water, giving the course and speed made good <u>over the ground</u>.

DR, on the other hand, is the course and speed <u>through the water</u>, and does not involve movement of the water itself.

So, any point along the track must be your EP for that time. You were quite right — well done!

Now plot the EP's for 1545 and 1600 on the chart if you have not already done so.

Then go to 187.

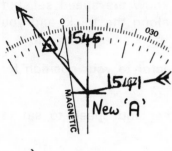

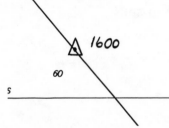

If you did not get these positions right, plot them again.

You estimate tidal stream will be 200°, 1 knot from 1541.

Your problem now is to find the course to steer and speed to set to make good 320° 10.1 knots.

Because the rendezvous is in half an hour, it is convenient to draw the triangle for half an hour which, of course, means drawing all speeds for half an hour.

As a first step, draw in the tidal stream vector.

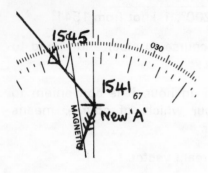

1545

030

1541 67

MAGNETIC

New 'A'

(Did you remember to draw the tidal stream for half an hour?)

Unlike the last example, you do not know the speed set, but you do know the speed made good along the track, and you have plotted your position for – 1611.

So join the end of the tidal stream vector to your position for 1611.

This line gives you the course to steer and speed to set to make good 320° speed 10·1 knots.

Measure the course to steer and speed to set.

Lay transparency 6 over the chart. Course is 325° speed 10·6 knots.

(Remember that the triangle has been drawn for half an hour, so the distance measured must be doubled to give the speed.)

Course 325°, speed 10·6 knots must take you through your rendezvous position, provided tidal stream remains constant.

You alter course and speed accordingly at 1541.

At 1557 you take the following fix:

Eddystone Lt	082°
Rame Hd (Chapel ruins)	035°
RHE St. George's Is	345°

Plot this.

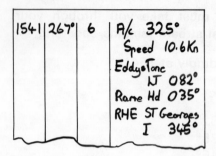

| 1541 | 267° | 6 | A/c 325°
Speed 10.6 Kn
EddystTone
N 082°
Rame Hd 035°
RHE ST Georges
I 345° |

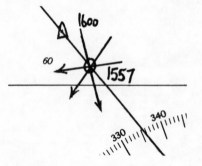

If you did not get the position right, plot it again.

At 1611 you will alter course to 280°, speed 12.

You now estimate that the tidal stream will be 207°, 0.8 knots from 1611.

Plot your 1641 EP.

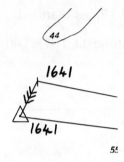

Draw in the track from 1611 to 1641.

What will be the course and speed made good between 1611 and 1641?

If you did not get the correct position, plot it again.

Course 276°
Speed 12·4 knots

Lay transparency 6 over
the chart

Did you remember to
plot your estimated
position along the track?
If not, do so now.

At 1611 you set course 280°, speed 12, as planned.

You take a visual bearing of Eddystone Lt 101½° and a radar range of the 6ʹ0.

Plot this position.

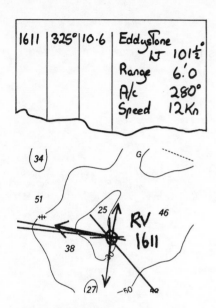

1611	325°	10.6	Eddystone
			LT 101½°
			Range 6.0
			A/c 280°
			Speed 12Kn

If you did not get this
position, plot it again.

At 1627 you take a bearing of Eddystone Lt as 100°. Radar
range 9.2.

Plot this.

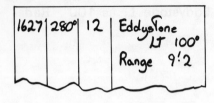

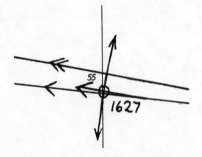

If you did not get this right,
plot it again.

The time is 1635.

You are ordered to rendezvous position:

50° 06:7 N

04° 50:7 W

at 1753.

Plot this position.

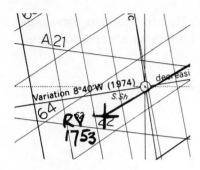

If you did not get this
right, plot it again.

You will alter course at 1641.

Draw in the track.

Measure the course and speed to be made good.

Course and speed to be made good are 240°, 10 knots.

Did you remember to plot your EP along the track?
If not, do so now.

Tidal stream set remains steady at 207°, but the rate increases to 1 knot. You must now determine course to steer and speed to set.

For what period of time will you draw the tidal stream triangle from your position at 1641?

For half an hour.   Go to 197.

For an hour.   Go to 198.

I'm not sure.   Go to 199.

You say that you will draw in the tidal stream triangle for half an hour.

It is quite possible to do this, and you would not be wrong if you did so. However, you always plot the tidal stream triangle which is most convenient for your purpose; also drawing a larger triangle means that you can make more accurate measurements.

Therefore, it is preferable to draw in the triangle for an hour. Since the rendezvous position is more than one hour of speed made good along the track, this is what you should do.

Now go to 200.

You say that you will draw in the tidal stream triangle for one hour.

Remember that you always draw in the tidal stream triangle which is most convenient for your purpose, and a larger triangle means that you can make more accurate measurements.

Obviously, since the rendezvous position is more than one hour of speed made good along the track, you will be quite correct in drawing the tidal stream triangle for one hour.

Now go to 200.

You say that you are not sure for what period of time you will draw the tidal stream triangle.

If you look at the two triangles so far plotted on the chart, you will see one drawn for an hour, the other for half an hour.

You should draw the triangle which is most practical and convenient, remembering that a larger triangle will enable you to make more accurate measurements.

Since, in this case, the rendezvous position is greater than one hour of speed made good along the track, you should draw in the triangle for one hour.

Now go to 200.

You now have to find the course to steer and speed to set to arrive at the rendezvous position at 1753.

First of all draw in the tidal stream vector for one hour and mark speed made good along the track.

Will you find the course to steer and speed to set by joining the end of the tidal stream vector to your rendezvous position at 1753, like this?

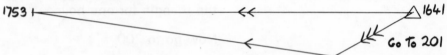

1753 ⊢ ⟨⟨ △ 1641

Go To 201

By marking off half an hour of speed made good and then joining the end of the tidal stream vector to this position, like this?

1753 ⊢ △ 1711 ⟨⟨ △ 1641

Go To 202

By marking off an hour of speed made good, and then joining the end of the tidal stream vector to this position, like this?

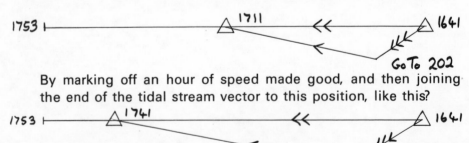

1753 ⊢ △ 1741 ⟨⟨ △ 1641

Go To 203

Your answer:

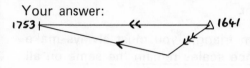

No, this is not the right answer.

When you draw a tidal stream triangle, you must always make sure that your <u>time and distance scales remain the same</u> on all three sides of the triangle.

Go back to 200 and choose again.

Your answer:

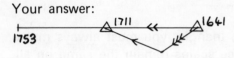

No, this is not the right answer.

When you draw a tidal stream triangle you must always make sure that your <u>time and distance scales remain the same</u> on all three sides of the triangle.

Go back to 200 and choose again.

Your answer:

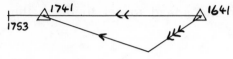

This is correct.

When you are drawing a tidal stream triangle you must always make sure that your <u>time and distance scales remain the same.</u>

What proportion of your speed made good would you mark off along the track if you had drawn the tidal stream vector for 40 minutes?

Go to 204.

You must mark off your
speed made good for 40
minutes along the track.

Now complete the tidal stream triangle on the chart.

What will be course to steer and speed to set to reach the
rendezvous position at 1753?

Course 243°
Speed 9·2 knots

(The distance to go from
1641 to 1753 is 12'0,
which requires a speed
made good of 10 knots.)

Lay transparency 7 over
the chart.

At 1638 you take the following fix:

Dodman Point Cross   273½°

Gribbin Hd Daymark   326°

Range of nearest
point of land on
bearing of Pen-a-maen 8'65

Plot this.

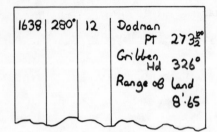

1638	280°	12	Dodman PT 273½°°
			Gribben Hd 326°
			Range of land 8'·65

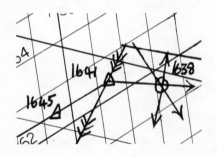

Chapter 5

At 1641 you alter course to 243°, 9·2 knots, as planned, (remember to note this in your notebook).

At 1700 the gyro alarm rings, indicating gyro failure.

You must now steer by magnetic compass.

Do you think that the magnetic compass course will be the same as the gyro-compass course?

Yes.   Go to 207.

No.   Go to 208.

I'm not sure. Go to 209.

You say that the magnetic compass course will be the same as the gyro-compass course.

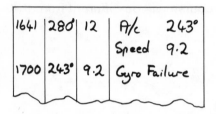

You probably know that the magnetic north pole is not at the geographical north pole (its position varies gradually from year to year).

Also, as ships are made of steel, the ship's structure will attract the magnetic compass needle.

So, in order for the ship to steam in the same direction, your magnetic compass course will be different from the gyro-compass course. So you have guessed wrong this time!

Go to 210.

You say that the magnetic compass course will be different from the gyro-compass course.

You probably know that the magnetic north pole is not at the geographical north pole. Also, as ships are made of steel, the ship's structure will attract the magnetic compass needle.

So you are quite right. In order for the ship to steam in the same direction, your magnetic compass course will be different from the gyro-compass course.

Go to page 210.

You say that you aren't sure whether the magnetic compass course will be the same as the gyro-compass course.

Well, you may know that the magnetic north pole is not the geographical north pole: its position varies gradually from year to year. Also, as ships are made of steel, the ship's structure will attract the magnetic compass needle.

So, in order for the ship to steam in the same direction, your magnetic course will be different from the gyro-compass course.

Go to 210.

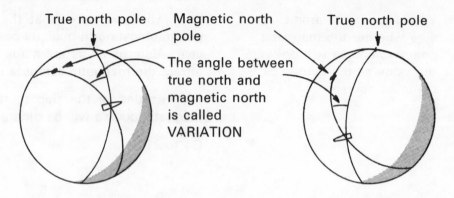

True north pole Magnetic north pole

The angle between true north and magnetic north is called VARIATION

True north pole

You can see from the diagram that the angle between the direction of true north and the direction of magnetic north will depend upon the geographical position of the ship.

Look at the chart, and see what the value of the variation was, in 1974, for a ship:

1.   South of Dodman Point.

2.   South East of Eddystone.

(Variation is usually marked on the compass rose printed on the chart.)

1.   8°40′W
2.   8°20′W
(Variation is usually
marked on the compass
rose printed on the chart.)

As the position of the magnetic pole changes so the amount of variation at a given position will change.

If your position is south of Dodman Point, what will be the amount of variation (to the nearest ¼°) for:

     1979
     1982
     1985

8¼° W
8° W
7¾° W

Look at this diagram:

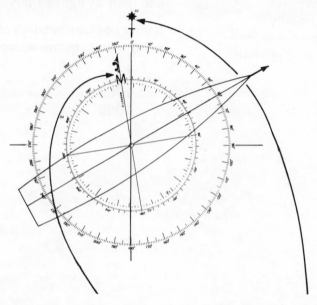

The magnetic north is 9° to the <u>west</u> of true north, hence the variation is 9° West.

The ship is steering 060° (T) (for True); to find the equivalent magnetic course we must add/subtract 9°. (To find out which, study the diagram.)

add

(The equivalent magnetic
course is 069°.)

Now look at this diagram:

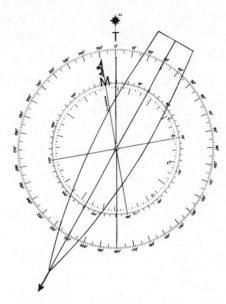

The variation is still 9°W. In whichever direction the ship is steering, we must still apply the variation in the same way.

Here, the ship is steering 210° (T). What is the equivalent magnetic course?

219°

So, we can deduce a rule:

If converting from a true course to a magnetic course we____ westerly variation.

add

Look now at this diagram:

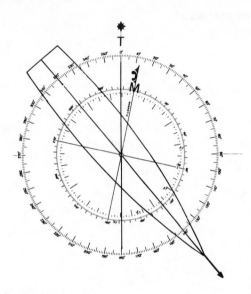

The magnetic north is 12° to the east of true north, hence the variation is 12° East.

The ship is steering 140° (T); to find the equivalent magnetic course we must add/subtract 12°. (Which?)

subtract

(The equivalent magnetic
course is 128°.)

Here is another diagram:

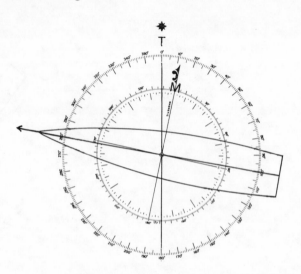

The variation is still 12° E. Again, you can see that in whichever
direction the ship is steering, you must still apply the variation the
same way.

Here, the ship is steering 280° (T).

What is the equivalent magnetic course?

268°

Our second rule is the reverse of the first one:

If converting from a true course to a magnetic course we
_____ easterly variation.

subtract

So we now have:

Converting from true to magnetic courses (or bearings):

1. add_____variation,
2. subtract_____variation.

add <u>westerly</u> variation

subtract <u>easterly</u> variation

If we convert from magnetic to true course we would expect to reverse our rules.

Look at the diagram to see if this is true.

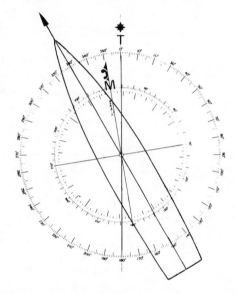

The ship is steering 339° (M). What is the equivalent true course?

330° (T)

Therefore, for converting from magnetic courses to true courses, we _____ westerly variation.

subtract

If, converting from magnetic courses to true courses we subtract westerly variation, then we must ___ _____ variation.

add easterly

We now have four rules:

Converting from true to magnetic compass courses (or bearings):

1.   add westerly variation,
2.   subtract easterly variation.

Converting from magnetic to true compass courses)or bearings):

3.   subtract westerly variation,
4.   add easterly variation.

Let us consider the question of converting bearings.

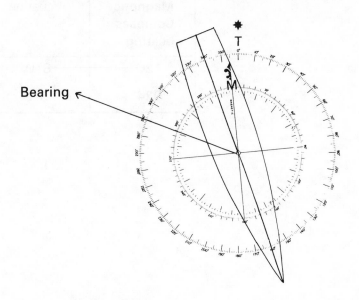

Bearing

The variation is 5°W. You can see from the diagram that the variation must be applied in the same way whether you are converting ship's head or a bearing.

If the magnetic bearing is 295° (M) what is the true bearing?

290° (T)

Now work out some examples:

Magnetic Compass bearing	Variation	True bearing
120°	8°W	?
024°	5°E	?

112°
(Compass to true <u>subtract</u>
westerly variation.)

029°
(Compass to true <u>add</u>
easterly variation.)

If you can remember one of the rules you can deduce the other three.

So, before you go to the next page, work out a mnemonic to help you remember one rule.
(There is a generally used mnemonic, which you will see on the next page; but you may think of a better one, and, in any case, working out one for yourself will help you to remember it.)

(If you thought of a good one, well done; but make sure that it is right! Check it with your instructor.)

The usual way to remember these rules is to say:

Compass ADd East to get True

shortened to:

CADET.

Compass here means the magnetic compass.

What is the reverse of this rule?

Compass to True Subtract West

or,

True to Compass Add West

or,

True to Compass Subtract East,

depending on what you thought was the reverse: all are correct of course.

You may wonder how often in this electronic age you will have to use the magnetic compass.

If you are navigating a warship or merchant vessel, then the answer is, only when the gyro breaks down, but then you will need to be thoroughly familiar with the magnetic compass.

Also, of course, you may have to navigate a boat or other small vessel which carries only a magnetic compass.

Now try several examples.

All these courses and bearings are magnetic — convert them to true.

021°(M)   Variation 4° E.
128°(M)   Variation 6° W.
256°(M)   Variation 3° W.
324°(M)   Variation 2° E.

025°
122°
253°
326°

(If you got any wrong,
turn back to 228 and work
out why. Remember CADET.)

All these courses and bearings are true. Convert them to magnetic.

006° Variation 6°W.
207° Variation 4°W.
351° Variation 2°E.
179° Variation 3°E.

012°(M)
211°(M)
349°(M)
176°(M)

(If you got any wrong,
turn back to 229 and work
out why. Remember CADET.)

So far we have only considered variation. But we have another error to consider.

The ship is made of metal and has its own magnetic field. This causes the compass needle to <u>deviate</u> from magnetic north, to the east or west.

The direction to which the compass needle points is called 'compass north'.

In this diagram, is compass north to the east, or west, of magnetic north?

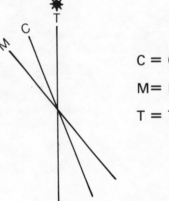

C = Compass north

M = Magnetic north

T = True north

east

(If you said west, remember that we asked whether compass north was to the east, or west, of magnetic north, not of true north.)

The angle between magnetic and compass north is called DEVIATION

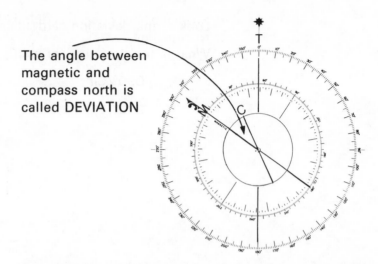

For reasons which we will not consider here, the amount of deviation varies with the course that the ship is steering. (The course is sometimes also called 'ship's head' i.e., the direction in which the head of the ship is pointing.)

The deviation card lists all deviations against ship's head. On what ship's head is there:

1.   Maximum easterly deviation?
2.   Maximum westerly deviation?

(You will find your deviation card in the envelope containing the transparencies.)

1.   260°

2.   080°

Look at the deviation card again.

What is the deviation for ship's head,

1.   090°(C)?

2.   310°(C)?

1.   13° W

2.   9° E

The ship's head on a deviation card is always ship's head by compass.

Deviation for a ship's head not on the card, can be found by interpolation.

The ship's head is 143°(C). Find the deviation to the nearest ¼°.

7¾°W

(Check with this section of the deviation card:

140°	8°W
150°	7°W

143° is $\frac{3}{10}$ of the way between 140° and 150°, so deviation must be $\frac{3}{10}$ of the way between 8° and 7°, which is 7.$\frac{7}{10}$° or 7¾° to the nearest ¼°.)

Now that you can find the deviation, the next thing to do is to be able to apply it.

This is easy, because as deviation and variation are both expressed as angles E or W of a meridian, then the same conversion rules will apply to both.

For instance, if you are converting a bearing of 115°(C) to a true bearing and the variation is 4°W and the deviation is 10½°W, you will _____ both the variation and deviation.

subtract

The true course would therefore be 115° −10½°, −4° =100½°.

You wish to convert a bearing of 300°(T) to a compass bearing. The variation is 20°W and the deviation is 10°E.

What is the compass bearing?

310°(C)

(300° + 20° − 10°)

We can use the diagram to confirm this:

Bearing taken

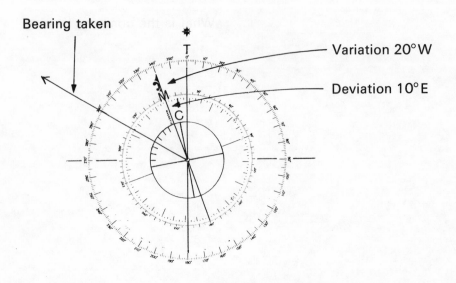

Variation 20°W

Deviation 10°E

If the bearing taken was 280°(C) what would be the true bearing?

270°

In converting from compass (C) to true (T) you have to apply both:

* deviation   [(C) to (M)]

   and

* variation   [(M) to (T)]

Therefore, the CADET rule covers both of these cases.

If the deviation is 6°E and the compass course is 152°(C), what is the magnetic course?

238

158°(M)

If you combine variation and deviation for any particular ship's head you obtain a <u>total compass error</u> that can be applied to any compass bearing.

If the ship's head (C) is 135°, the variation is 10° E, and the deviation is 8½° W, what is the total compass error?

1½°E

Now look at the chart.

Your course is 243(T) + 7½°W − 12°E = 238½°(C)

At 1700:

Dodman Pt Cross	284½°(C)
Mevagissey Lt	309½°(C)
Gribben Hd (Daymark)	348½°(C)

Convert these to true bearings to the bearest ½° − remember the word CADET. (Use variation for 1985 for a point midway between the 2 compass roses.)

240

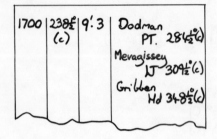

1700	238½ (c)	9'.3	Dodman PT. 284½°(c)
			Mevagissey LT 309½°(c)
			Gribben Hd 348½°(c)

Plot the fix at 1700.

Dodman Pt   289°(T)
Mevagissey Lt   314°(T)
Gribben Hd   353°(T)

(Variation 7½°W
Deviation 12°E)

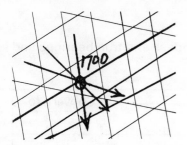

Test

Here is a brief test for you to practise working out conversions between compass and true bearings and courses. Give your answers to the nearest ½°.

	Ship's head (Course)	Variation	Bearings	Convert to
1.	312°(C)	4°W	268°(C) 105°(C)	True bearings
2.	212°(C)	13°E	—	True course
3.	085°(C)	2°E	151°(C) 018°(C) 224°(C)	True bearings

Answers to Test

	Ship's head (Course)	Convert	Variation	Deviation	Answer
1.	312°(C)	268°(C) 105°(C) to true bearings	4°W (subtract) (compass to true subtract west)	8½°E (add) [ship's head 312°(C)]	272½°(T) 109½°(T)
2.	212°(C)	To true course	13°E (add) (compass to true add east)	7½°E (add) [(ship's head 212°(C)]	232½°(T)
3.	185°(C)	151°(C) 018°(C) 224°(C) to true bearings	2°E (add) (compass to true add east)	13½°W (subtract)	139½°(T) 006½°(T) 212½°(T)

(1 mark for each answer— total of 6. If you got less than 4 go back to page 212 and read the section again.)

You can now convert between true and compass bearings, using ship's head (C).

If, however, we convert from true ship's head to compass ship's head we have another problem.

We can find the variation by looking at the chart, but to find the deviation we need to know the ship's head (C).

Course   030°(T)

Variation   10°W

Can we now find the deviation?

No
(Because we do not yet
know the ship's head (C).)

We cannot find the deviation without knowing the ship's head (C), but we cannot convert to ship's head (C) without knowing the deviation!

If we could read off the correct deviation in some other way our problem would be solved.

If we apply the deviation to the ship's head (C), what will we get?

Ship's head (M)
(That is, with only
variation applied.)

Look on the deviation card.

You will notice that there is a third column on the card, headed Ship's Head (M).

Complete this column in the part of the deviation card shown below.

Ship's Head (C)	Deviation	Ship's Head (M)
030°	7°W	
040°	9°W	
050°	11°W	
060°	12°W	

Ship's Head (C)	Deviation	Ship's Head (M)
030°	7°W	023°
040°	9°W	031°
050°	11°W	039°
060°	12°W	048°

Now fill in all the rest of the ship's head (M) column.

Ship's Head (Compass)	Deviation	Ship's Head (Magnetic)
000°	2°W	358°
010°	4°W	006°
020°	5°W	015°
030°	7°W	023°
040°	9°W	031°
050°	11°W	039°
060°	12°W	048°
070°	13°W	057°
080°	14°W	066°
090°	13°W	077°
100°	12°W	088°
110°	11°W	099°
120°	10°W	110°
130°	9°W	121°
140°	8°W	132°
150°	7°W	143°
160°	5°W	155°
170°	3°W	167°
180°	0°W	10°
190°	3°E	193°
200°	5°E	205°
210°	7°E	217°
220°	9°E	229°
230°	11°E	241°
240°	12°E	252°
250°	13°E	263°
260°	14°E	274°
270°	13°E	283°
280°	12°E	292°
290°	11°E	301°
300°	10°E	310°
310°	9°E	319°
320°	7°E	327°
330°	5°E	335°
340°	3°E	343°
350°	1°E	351°

When we know the ship's head (M), we can read off the deviation directly against it.

In the example that we have just worked out, the ship's head (T) was 030°, and the variation 10°W. What was the ship's head (M)?

040°(M)

If we look again at the part of our deviation card:

Ship's Head (C)	Deviation	Ship's Head (M)
030°	7°W	023°
040°	9°W	031°
050°	11°W	039°
060°	12°W	048°

We see that for a ship's head of 040°(M), the deviation is 11°W, giving a compass course of 040° + 11° = 051°(C).

Now, try another one. If your course is 325°(T), and variation is 8°W, what is your compass course?

(Remember, use the ship's head (M) column to find the deviation.)

327½°(C)

(i)　Ship's head (M) is
　　325° + 8° = 333°

Ship's Head (C)	Deviation	Ship's Head (M)
310°	9°W	319°
320°	7°E	327°
330°	5°E	335°
340°	3°E	343°

(ii)　Deviation is therefore 5½°E.

(iii)　Ship's head (C) is
　　333° − 5½° = 327½°(C).

At sea you will find that almost all deviations will only vary between about 0° and 3° over the whole card, and so ship's head (M) and ship's head (C) will be very similar.

You may also find that deviation cards in use at sea have not yet been converted to have a third column.

Remember too, you do not need to use this system when converting from ship's head (C) to ship's head (T), because you can read off the right deviation straight away against ship's head (C).

Turn to 251 for further practice.

Test

Give your answers to the nearest ½°.

	Ship's head (Course)	Variation	Bearings	Convert to
1.	078°(T)	7°E	–	Compass course
2.	346°(T)	11°E	350°(C) 074°(C)	True bearings
3.	135°(C)	10°W	–	True course
4.	245°(T)	13°W	–	Compass course

Answers to Test

	Ship's head (Course)	Convert	Variation	Deviation	Answer
1.	078°(T)	To compass course	7°E (subtract) (True to compass subtract east)	13½°W	084½°(C)
2.	346°(T) = 335°(M) = 330°(C)	350°(C) 074°(C) to true bearing	11°E (add) (Compass to true add east)	5°E	006°(T) 090°(T)
3.	135°(C)	To true course	10°W (subtract) (Compass to true subtract west)	8½°W	116½°(T)
4.	245°(T)	To compass course	13°W (add) (True to compass add west)	12½°E	245½°(C)

If you made any mistakes in questions 1, 2 or 4, go back to page 244 and read the sequence again.

Let us briefly revise all definitions.

In order to convert compass course to true course, we must apply _____ and _____ .

variation
and
deviation

Define variation.

Variation is the angle
between magnetic north
and true north.

Define deviation.

Deviation is the angle between compass north and magnetic north.

If you take a fix you will find the value of the deviation against which of the following?

(a)   Each bearing

(b)   Ship's head

(b) Ship's head

At 1718 the range by radar of Dodman Pt is 4.75.

The compass bearing of Dodman Pt Cross is 311½°(C).

Plot this position.

| 1718 | 238½° (c) | 9.3 | Dodman Pt
311½°(c)
Range 4'·75 |

(True bearing of
Dodman Pt is 316°(T).)

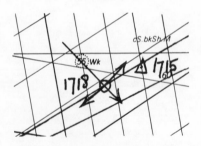

If you did not get the correct
position, plot it again.

At 1736 you take the following Decca fix:

Red   A19·6   or   50° 08'·15N
Green G37·0   04° 46'·75W

Plot this.

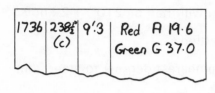

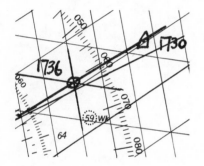

If you did not get the correct
position, plot it again.

The time is now 1745.

At 1753 you will alter course to rendezvous at:

  50° 07:55N
  04° 32:0W at 1853

What will be the true course and speed to be made good from
1753?

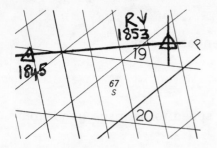

Course 086°(T),

Speed 12.

> Did you remember to plot
> your EP ahead? If not do
> so now, and use the
> symbol ⚠ .

You then estimate that tidal stream will then be 210°, 1·2 knots.

Your gyro-compass has still not settled.

What is the compass course (to the nearest degree) to steer from 1753 (for the year 1985).

What speed will you set?

102°(C)

12·7 knots

[True course   082°(T)
Variation   7¾°W
Ship's Head (M) 089° ¾°(M)
Deviation   12°W
Compass Course   102°(C)]
(to the nearest degree)

At 1753 you alter course 102°(C), speed 12·7 knots as planned. At 1805 your position by Decca is:

Red   A21·2   50° 06'·85N
Green   G38·0   or   04° 46'·9W

Plot this.

| 1753 | 238½° (c) | 9.3 | A/c 102° (c) |
| 1805 | 102° (c) | 12.7 | Red A 21.2
Green G 38.0 |

At 1850 you take a bearing of LHE Dodman Pt 319½°(C), and radar range 11·0.

Convert to a true bearing and plot the fix.

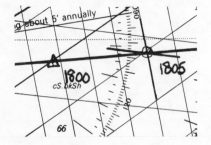

If you did not get this right, plot the position again.

Remember, a Decca position is a fix, and must be marked with the correct symbol ⊙.

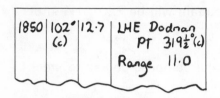

1850	102° (c)	12·7	LHE Dodman
			Pt 319½° (c)
			Range 11·0

(True bearing of LHE
Dodman Pt 300°(T).)
(Did you remember to use
the ship's head (M) for
the deviation?)

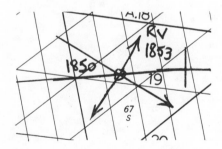

At 1853 you are to set a course which will take you to position 'B',
bearing 135°(T) Eddystone Lt 7'·0.

Plot this position.

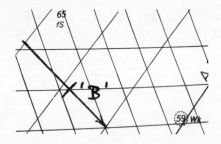

If you did not get this position right, plot it again.

You then estimate that the tidal stream will be 220°, 1½ knots.

Your speed will be 12 knots.

Now determine, by construction, the compass course to steer.

Compass Course 108½(C)

[True Course   090°(T)
Variation   7½°(W)
Ship's Head   ―――――
(M)   097½°(M)
Deviation   11°(W)
Compass Course   108½(C)]

Measure speed made good along the track, and plot your position every quarter of an hour.

11·1 knots.

Lay transparency 8 over the chart and check your construction.

At 1853 you alter course as planned. Your gyro is now functioning properly, so you set true course 090°(T).

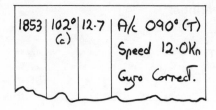

| 1853 | 102°
(c) | 12.7 | A/c 090° (T)
Speed 12.0Kn
Gyro Correct. |

The time is 1905.

You take the following bearings:

> Gribben Hd Daymark   327°(T)
> RHE ST George's I   005°(T)
> Eddystone Lt   067°(T)

Plot this.

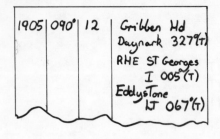

| 1905 | 090° | 12 | Gribben Hd Daymark 327°(T)
RHE ST Georges I 005°(T)
Eddystone Lt 067°(T) |

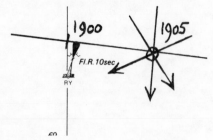

At 1935 you take the following bearings:

RHE St George's I	342°(T)
Eddystone Lt	033°(T)
Range 4·85(M)	

Plot this.

If you did not get this right,
plot it again.

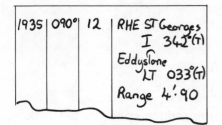

| 1935 | 090° | 12 | RHE St Georges I 342°(T) Eddystone LT 033°(T) Range 4'·90 |

At 2005 you take the following bearings:

Eddystone Lt   329°(T) Range 5'·50 (M)
Mewstone   015°(T)

Plot this.

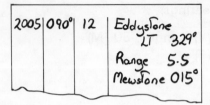

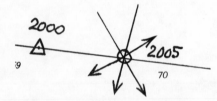

Chapter 6

At 2015 you set course 010° for Plymouth.

Visibility has closed in again, so you reduce speed to 6 knots.

You estimate that tidal stream is 248°, 0·8 knots.

Plot your EP until 2115.

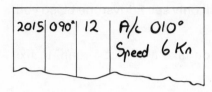

2015	090°	12	A/c 010° Speed 6 Kn

Lay transparency 9 over
the chart and check your
plotting.

It is 2030. The bearing of Eddystone Lt is 305°.

Plot this.

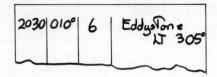

Because of poor visibility you can still only see Eddystone Lt, so you decide to take a running fix.

Describe in your own words how you take and plot a running fix.

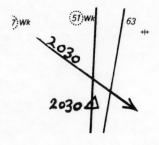

Your answer should mean the same as the one given below.

Take two bearings of the same object at different times. Transfer the first bearing through the ship's DR position at the time of the second bearing.

At 2100 the bearing of Eddystone is 277°.

Plot this.

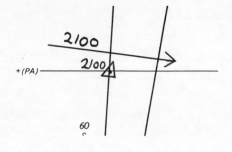

When you took your first running fix, you plotted a new 1225 DR starting from the first position line (at 1210) and transferred it through the new DR position (at 1225).

Now that there is a tidal stream do you think that you should transfer the 2030 position through:

(a) a new 2100 EP?   Go to 275.

(b) a new 2100 DR?   Go to 276.

You say that you should transfer your 2030 position line through your 2100 EP.

If you plot the transferred position line through a different position, you will get a different fix:

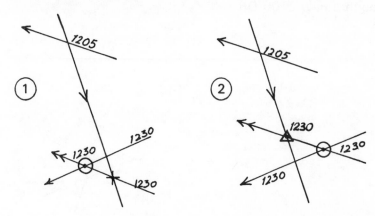

So the position through which you transfer the first position line must be your <u>best estimate</u> of the ship's position, that is, the EP.

So you were right. Plot a new 2100 EP, starting from the 2030 position line and transfer this position line through it.

Do this now and then go to 277.

You say that you should transfer your 2030 position line through a new 2100 DR position.

If you plot the transferred position line through a different position, you will get a different fix.

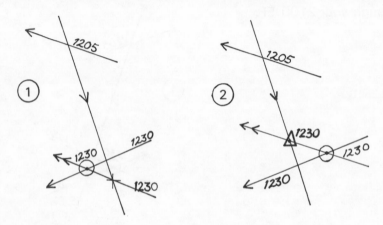

So the position through which you transfer the first position line must be your <u>best estimate</u> of the ship's position, that is, the EP.

So you were wrong.

Plot a new 2100 EP, starting from the 2030 position line, and transfer this position line through it.

Do this now and then go to 277.

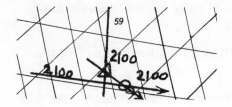

You have fixed your position for 2100 by running fix, so now plot your EP for 2115 again.

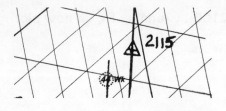

From your position at 2115 you are to make good a course of 350½°
to take you into Plymouth Sound.

You want to pass through a position from which Penlee Pt bears
270° 1ʹ0 at 2145.

If the tidal stream will be 270°, 0·7 knots, what will be the speed to
set and course to steer from 2115?

353°, 15·0 knots

Lay transparency 11 over the chart and check your plotting.

At 2115 you alter course to 353°, 15·0 knots, as planned. At 2133 you take the following transit:

LHE Rame Hd Ø
Portwrinkle Tr 315°

What is the error of your gyro compass?

[Error is expressed as low (L) or high (H).]

2°(H)

(The true bearing of the transit is 313°.)

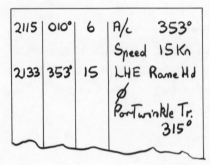

| 2115 | 010° | 6 | A/c 353° |
| 2133 | 353° | 15 | Speed 15 Kn |

Since your gyro is now 2° high, should you now tell the helmsman to steer:

1.   351°?

or

2.   355°?

355°

(If you got this right,
well done. If you did not,
remember that if you steer
351° and your gyro is 2°
high, your true course is
349°.)

In practice, at sea, you would now apply this error to all bearings and courses, until a further check showed that the error had changed or disappeared.

You can see from the chart that your course from 2130 takes you close to the shoals off Penlee Pt.

As a safety measure you must not at any time be within a range of 0.5 of Penlee Pt. The ship will then not get closer than 0.3 from the shoals.

So draw an arc of a circle, radius 0.5 from Penlee Pt.

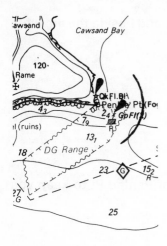

44

This arc gives you the minimum range of Penlee Pt which will take you clear of the shoals.

It is therefore called the _____ing range.

clearing range

At each end of the arc draw an arrowhead, and beside the arc write the range, like this:

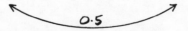

Is this the minimum or maximum range of Penlee Pt to keep you clear of the shoals?

the minimum range

Since this is the minimum range, the range must be NOT LESS than 0·5.

Therefore, write the letters N.L. beside the range, like this:

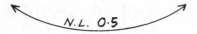

What abbreviation would we have used if this had been the maximum range to keep us clear of the shoals?

N.M.
(Not More than)

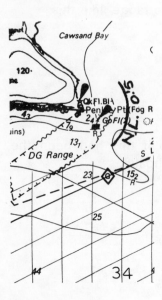

So, if your range of Penlee Pt is not less than 0˙5, you must be safe from the shoals.

It may not always be possible to use a clearing range.

Look at the chart.

If you draw 8 metres, what danger is there just east of Tinker Buoy?

A 3·7 metre patch.

You need a rapid check to see that you keep clear of Tinker patch (assuming that the buoy is not on station).

Draw a bearing of the Breakwater Light of 340°.

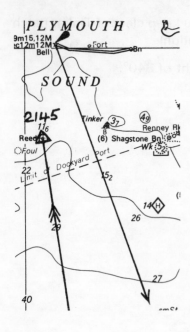

If you look at the bearing you have just drawn, you will see that it is clear of the Tinker patch to the west.

In the same way that the range of Penlee Pt was a clearing range, the bearing of the Breakwater Lt is a _____ bearing.

clearing

Provided that your bearing of Breakwater Lt is not ____ than 340°, you must be clear of Tinker patch. (You would, of course, have to take into account gyro error if you still had such an error.)

not <u>less</u>

(If the bearing *is* less, you
will be to the east of the
line you have drawn on
the chart.)

So you should mark this bearing, N._. 340°.

N.L

So, your clearing bearing of the Breakwater Lt is NL 340°.

Mark accordingly the bearing you have drawn.

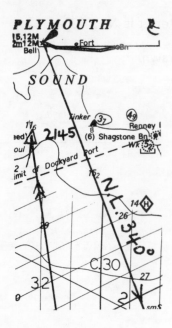

You are now approaching the end of your journey.

Your final step before entering Plymouth will be to transfer your position to a larger scale chart of the harbour.

It is very important that you do this correctly, so you will have to plot your position by one method, and_____it by another.

check
(confirm)

You decide to transfer to the larger scale chart from a position 151°
Penlee Pt Lt 2′9.

Plot this.

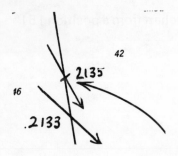

You will now need to check that you have correctly transferred this position to the next chart.

How could you do this?

If your position is not here, plot it again.

Plot the same position by
latitude and longitude.

What is the latitude and longitude of the position?

50° 16.5 N

04° 09.2 W

So you will transfer your position to the larger scale chart of Plymouth Sound by plotting it by range and bearing from Penlee Pt., and then _____ it by latitude and longitude.

checking

You have now come to the end of your journey and of the programme.

You can now use all the normal techniques of plotting on a chart and should be ready to practise them at sea.

Notes

Notes

Notes

Notes

Notes

Notes

Notes